SCHIZOPHRENIA

•   •   •   •   •   •   •

GENERAL EDITORS

Dale C. Garell, M.D.

Medical Director, California Childrens Services, County of Los Angeles
Clinical Professor, Department of Pediatrics & Family Medicine,
    University of Southern California School of Medicine
Associate Clinical Professor, Maternal & Child Health, School of Public
    Health, University of Hawaii
Former president, Society for Adolescent Medicine

Solomon H. Snyder, M.D.

Distinguished Service Professor of Neuroscience, Pharmacology, and
    Psychiatry, Johns Hopkins University School of Medicine
Former president, Society of Neuroscience
Albert Lasker Award in Medical Research, 1978

CONSULTING EDITORS

Robert W. Blum, M.D.

Associate Professor, School of Public Health and Department of
    Pediatrics; Director, Adolescent Health Program;
    University of Minnesota

Charles E. Irwin, Jr., M.D.

Associate Professor of Pediatrics, Division of Adolescent Medicine,
    University of California, San Francisco

Lloyd J. Kolbe, Ph.D.

Chief, Office of School Health & Special Projects, Centers for
    Disease Control

Jordan J. Popkin

Director, Division of Federal Employee Occupational Health, U.S. Public
    Health Service

Joseph L. Rauh, M.D.

Professor of Pediatrics, Adolescent Clinic, Children's Hospital Medical
    Center, Cincinnati

THE ENCYCLOPEDIA OF
H E A L T H

PSYCHOLOGICAL DISORDERS
AND THEIR TREATMENT
SOLOMON H. SNYDER, M.D. · GENERAL EDITOR

SCHIZOPHRENIA

Patrick Young

Introduction by C. Everett Koop, M.D., Sc.D.
Surgeon General, U.S. Public Health Service

CHELSEA HOUSE PUBLISHERS
New York · Philadelphia

CHELSEA HOUSE PUBLISHERS
New York · Philadelphia

The goal of the ENCYCLOPEDIA OF HEALTH *is to provide general information in the ever-changing areas of physiology, psychology, and related medical issues. The titles in this series are not intended to take the place of the professional advice of a physician or other health-care professional.*

EDITOR-IN-CHIEF: Nancy Toff
EXECUTIVE EDITOR: Remmel T. Nunn
MANAGING EDITOR: Karyn Gullen Browne
COPY CHIEF: Juliann Barbato
PICTURE EDITOR: Adrian G. Allen
ART DIRECTOR: Giannella Garrett
MANUFACTURING MANAGER: Gerald Levine

Staff for *Schizophrenia*:
SENIOR EDITOR: Jane Larkin Crain
ASSISTANT EDITOR: James Cornelius
COPY EDITOR: Terrance Dolan
DEPUTY COPY CHIEF: Ellen Scordato
EDITORIAL ASSISTANTS: Nicole Bowen, Susan DeRosa
ASSOCIATE PICTURE EDITOR: Juliette Dickstein
PICTURE RESEARCHER: Linda Peer
DESIGN: Debby Jay, Jean Weiss
DESIGNER: Victoria Tomaselli
ASSISTANT DESIGNERS: Donna Sinisgalli, Ghila Krajzman
PRODUCTION COORDINATOR: Joseph Romano

COVER ILLUSTRATION—SCULPTURE AND PHOTO: Linda Peer

5 7 9 8 6 4

Library of Congress Cataloging in Publication Data

Young, Patrick.
  Schizophrenia.
  (The Encyclopedia of health)
  Bibliography: p.
  Includes index.
  1. Schizophrenia.   I. Title.   II. Series.
RC514.Y68   1988   616.89'82   88-1052
ISBN 0-7910-0052-4
    0-7910-0515-1 (pbk.)

CONTENTS

THE ENCYCLOPEDIA OF
H E A L T H

THE HEALTHY BODY

The Circulatory System
Dental Health
The Digestive System
The Endocrine System
Exercise
Genetics & Heredity
The Human Body: An Overview
Hygiene
The Immune System
Memory & Learning
The Musculoskeletal System
The Nervous System
Nutrition
The Reproductive System
The Respiratory System
The Senses
Speech & Hearing
Sports Medicine
Vision
Vitamins & Minerals

THE LIFE CYCLE

Adolescence
Adulthood
Aging
Childhood
Death & Dying
The Family
Friendship & Love
Pregnancy & Birth

MEDICAL ISSUES

Careers in Health Care
Environmental Health
Folk Medicine
Health Care Delivery
Holistic Medicine
Medical Ethics
Medical Fakes & Frauds
Medical Technology
Medicine & the Law
Occupational Health
Public Health

PYSCHOLOGICAL DISORDERS
AND THEIR TREATMENT

Anxiety & Phobias
Child Abuse
Compulsive Behavior
Delinquency & Criminal Behavior
Depression
Diagnosing & Treating Mental Illness
Eating Habits & Disorders
Learning Disabilities
Mental Retardation
Personality Disorders
Schizophrenia
Stress Management
Suicide

MEDICAL DISORDERS
AND THEIR TREATMENT

AIDS
Allergies
Alzheimer's Disease
Arthritis
Birth Defects
Cancer
The Common Cold
Diabetes
Emergency Medicine
Gynecological Disorders
Headaches
The Hospital
Kidney Disorders
Medical Diagnosis
The Mind-Body Connection
Mononucleosis and Other Infectious Diseases
Nuclear Medicine
Organ Transplants
Pain
Physical Handicaps
Poisons & Toxins
Prescription & OTC Drugs
Sexually Transmitted Diseases
Skin Disorders
Stroke & Heart Disease
Substance Abuse
Tropical Medicine

PREVENTION AND EDUCATION: THE KEYS TO GOOD HEALTH

C. Everett Koop, M.D., Sc.D.
Surgeon General,
U.S. Public Health Service

The issue of health education has received particular attention in recent years because of the presence of AIDS in the news. But our response to this particular tragedy points up a number of broader issues that doctors, public health officials, educators, and the public face. In particular, it points up the necessity for sound health education for citizens of all ages.

Over the past 25 years this country has been able to bring about dramatic declines in the death rates for heart disease, stroke, accidents, and, for people under the age of 45, cancer. Today, Americans generally eat better and take better care of themselves than ever before. Thus, with the help of modern science and technology, they have a better chance of surviving serious—even catastrophic—illnesses. That's the good news.

But, like every phonograph record, there's a flip side, and one with special significance for young adults. According to a report issued in 1979 by Dr. Julius Richmond, my predecessor as Surgeon General, Americans aged 15 to 24 had a higher death rate in 1979 than they did 20 years earlier. The causes: violent death and injury, alcohol and drug abuse, unwanted pregnancies, and sexually transmitted diseases. Adolescents are particularly vulnerable, because they are beginning to explore their own sexuality and perhaps to experiment with drugs. The need for educating young people is critical, and the price of neglect is high.

Yet even for the population as a whole, our health is still far from what it could be. Why? A 1974 Canadian government report attributed all death and disease to four broad elements: inadequacies in the health-care system, behavioral factors or unhealthy life-styles, environmental hazards, and human biological factors.

To be sure, there are diseases that are still beyond the control of even our advanced medical knowledge and techniques. And despite yearnings that are as old as the human race itself, there is no "fountain of youth" to ward off aging and death. Still, there is a solution to many of the problems that undermine sound health. In a word, that solution is prevention. Prevention, which includes health promotion and education, saves lives, improves the quality of life, and, in the long run, saves money.

In the United States, organized public health activities and preventive medicine have a long history. Important milestones include the improvement of sanitary procedures and the development of pasteurized milk in the late 19th century, and the introduction in the mid-20th century of effective vaccines against polio, measles, German measles, mumps, and other once-rampant diseases. Internationally, organized public health efforts began on a wide-scale basis with the International Sanitary Conference of 1851, to which 12 nations sent representatives. The World Health Organization, founded in 1948, continues these efforts under the aegis of the United Nations, with particular emphasis on combatting communicable diseases and the training of health-care workers.

But despite these accomplishments, much remains to be done in the field of prevention. For too long, we have had a medical care system that is science- and technology-based, focused, essentially, on illness and mortality. It is now patently obvious that both the social and the economic costs of such a system are becoming insupportable.

Implementing prevention—and its corollaries, health education and promotion—is the job of several groups of people:

First, the medical and scientific professions need to continue basic scientific research, and here we are making considerable progress. But increased concern with prevention will also have a decided impact on how primary-care doctors practice medicine. With a shift to health-based rather than morbidity-based medicine, the role of the "new physician" will include a healthy dose of patient education.

Second, practitioners of the social and behavioral sciences—psychologists, economists, city planners—along with lawyers, business leaders, and government officials—must solve the practical and ethical dilemmas confronting us: poverty, crime, civil rights, literacy, education, employment, housing, sanitation, environmental protection, health care delivery systems, and so forth. All of these issues affect public health.

Third is the public at large. We'll consider that very important group in a moment.

Fourth, and the linchpin in this effort, is the public health profession—doctors, epidemiologists, teachers—who must harness the professional expertise of the first two groups and the common sense and cooperation of the third, the public. They must define the problems statistically and qualitatively and then help us set priorities for finding the solutions.

To a very large extent, improving those statistics is the responsibility of every individual. So let's consider more specifically what the role of the individual should be and why health education is so important to that role. First, and most obviously, individuals can protect themselves from illness and injury and thus minimize their need for professional medical care. They can eat a nutritious diet, get adequate exercise, avoid tobacco, alcohol, and drugs, and take prudent steps to avoid accidents. The proverbial "apple a day keeps the doctor away" is not so far from the truth, after all.

Second, individuals should actively participate in their own medical care. They should schedule regular medical and dental checkups. Should they develop an illness or injury, they should know when to treat themselves and when to seek professional help. To gain the maximum benefit from any medical treatment that they do require, individuals must become partners in that treatment. For instance, they should understand the effects and side effects of medications. I counsel young physicians that there is no such thing as too much information when talking with patients. But the corollary is the patient must know enough about the nuts and bolts of the healing process to understand what the doctor is telling him. That is at least partially the patient's responsibility.

Education is equally necessary for us to understand the ethical and public policy issues in health care today. Sometimes individuals will encounter these issues in making decisions about their own treatment or that of family members. Other citizens may encounter them as jurors in medical malpractice cases. But we all become involved, indirectly, when we elect our public officials, from school board members to the president. Should surrogate parenting be legal? To what extent is drug testing desirable, legal, or necessary? Should there be public funding for family planning, hospitals, various types of medical research, and medical care for the indigent? How should we allocate scant technological resources, such as kidney dialysis and organ transplants? What is the proper role of government in protecting the rights of patients?

What are the broad goals of public health in the United States today? In 1980, the Public Health Service issued a report aptly entitled *Promoting Health-Preventing Disease: Objectives for the Nation.* This report expressed its goals in terms of mortality and in terms of intermediate goals in education and health improvement. It identified 15 major concerns: controlling high blood pressure; improving family planning; improving pregnancy care and infant health; increasing the rate of immunization; controlling sexually transmitted diseases; controlling the presence of toxic agents and radiation in the environment; improving occupational safety and health; preventing accidents; promoting water fluoridation and dental health; controlling infectious diseases; decreasing smoking; decreasing alcohol and drug abuse; improving nutrition; promoting physical fitness and exercise; and controlling stress and violent behavior.

For healthy adolescents and young adults (ages 15 to 24), the specific goal was a 20% reduction in deaths, with a special focus on motor vehicle injuries and alcohol and drug abuse. For adults (ages 25 to 64), the aim was 25% fewer deaths, with a concentration on heart attacks, strokes, and cancers.

Smoking is perhaps the best example of how individual behavior can have a direct impact on health. Today cigarette smoking is recognized as the most important single preventable cause of death in our society. It is responsible for more cancers and more cancer deaths than any other known agent; is a prime risk factor for heart and blood vessel disease, chronic bronchitis, and emphysema; and is a frequent cause of complications in pregnancies and of babies born prematurely, underweight, or with potentially fatal respiratory and cardiovascular problems.

Since the release of the Surgeon General's first report on smoking in 1964, the proportion of adult smokers has declined substantially, from 43% in 1965 to 30.5% in 1985. Since 1965, 37 million people have quit smoking. Although there is still much work to be done if we are to become a "smoke-free society," it is heartening to note that public health and public education efforts—such as warnings on cigarette packages and bans on broadcast advertising—have already had significant effects.

In 1835, Alexis de Tocqueville, a French visitor to America, wrote, "In America the passion for physical well-being is general." Today, as then, health and fitness are front-page items. But with the greater scientific and technological resources now available to us, we are in a far stronger position to make good health care available to everyone. And with the greater technological threats to us as we approach the 21st century, the need to do so is more urgent than ever before. Comprehensive information about basic biology, preventive medicine, medical and surgical treatments, and related ethical and public policy issues can help you arm yourself with the knowledge you need to be healthy throughout your life.

FOREWORD

Solomon H. Snyder, M.D.

Mental disorders represent the number one health problem for the United States and probably for the entire human population. Some studies estimate that approximately one-third of all Americans suffer from some sort of emotional disturbance. Depression of varying severity will affect as many as 20 percent of all of us at one time or another in our lives. Severe anxiety is even more common.

Adolescence is a time of particular susceptibility to emotional problems. Teenagers are undergoing significant changes in their brain as well as their physical structure. The hormones that alter the organs of reproduction during puberty also influence the way we think and feel. At a purely psychological level, adolescents must cope with major upheavals in their lives. After years of not noticing the opposite sex, they find themselves romantically attracted but must painfully learn the skills of social interchange both for superficial, flirtatious relationships and for genuine intimacy. Teenagers must develop new ways of relating to their parents. Adolescents strive for independence. Yet, our society is structured in such a way that teenagers must remain dependent on their parents for many more years. During adolescence, young men and women examine their own intellectual bents and begin to plan the type of higher education and vocation they believe they will find most fulfilling.

Because of all these challenges, teenagers are more emotionally volatile than adults. Passages from extreme exuberance to dejection are common. The emotional distress of completely normal adolescence can be so severe that the same disability in an adult would be labeled as major mental illness. Although most teenagers somehow muddle through and emerge unscathed, a number of problems are more frequent among adolescents than among adults. Many psychological aberrations reflect severe disturbances, although these are sometimes not regarded as "psychiatric." Eating disorders, to which young adults are especially vulnerable, are an example. An extremely large number of teenagers diet to great excess even though they are not overweight. Many of them suffer from a specific disturbance referred to as anorexia nervosa, a form of self-starvation that is just as real a disorder as diabetes. The same is true for those who eat compulsively and then sometimes force themselves to vomit. They may be afflicted with bulimia.

Depression is also surprisingly frequent among adolescents, although its symptoms may be less obvious in young people than they are in adults. And, because suicide occurs most frequently in those suffering from depression, we must be on the lookout for subtle hints of despondency in those close to us. This is especially urgent because teenage suicide is a rapidly worsening national problem.

The volumes on Psychological Disorders and Their Treatment in the ENCYCLOPEDIA OF HEALTH cover the major areas of mental illness, from mild to severe. They also emphasize the means available for getting help. *Anxiety and Phobias, Depression,* and *Schizophrenia* deal specifically with these forms of mental disturbance. *Child Abuse* and *Delinquency and Criminal Behavior* explore abnormalities of behavior that may stem from environmental and social influences as much as from biological or psychological illness. *Personality Disorders* and *Compulsive Behavior* explain how people develop disturbances of their overall personality. *Learning Disabilities* investigates disturbances of the mind that may reflect neurological derangements as much as psychological abnormalities. *Mental Retardation* explains the various causes of this many-sided handicap, including the genetic component, complications during pregnancy, and traumas during birth. *Suicide* discusses the epidemiology of this tragic phenomenon and outlines the assistance available to those who are at risk. *Stress Management* locates the sources of stress in contemporary society and considers formal strategies for coping with it. Finally, *Diagnosing and Treating Mental Illness* explains to the reader how professionals sift through various signs and symptoms to define the exact nature of the various mental disorders and fully describes the most effective means of alleviating them.

Fortunately, when it comes to psychological disorders, knowing the facts is a giant step toward solving the problems.

·   ·   ·   ·

CHAPTER 1

. . . .

A LASTING
MADNESS

The Madhouse (Bedlam) by William Hogarth

Schizophrenia is almost universally viewed as the classic example of madness. For many people, the word *crazy* brings to mind the strange and often bizarre behavior of schizophrenics—the delusions, hallucinations, and incoherent talk so common among its victims. It is a startling experience to unexpectedly come upon a person who proclaims himself Jesus Christ, rants gibberish, or sits with his body unmoving as if frozen in time and place. For some people, such an experience is too shocking, too fearsome, too repulsive. They hurry away, trying to dismiss the image of the deranged individual from their minds.

13

No psychiatric disorder is as disabling and baffling as schizophrenia. It cripples the mind and a person's ability to function as surely as a severed spinal cord cripples the body. Today, in spite of the drugs that have allowed many schizophrenics to live at home or in the community, a significant number of people admitted to mental hospitals are victims of the disease. Schizophrenics account for nearly 40% of admissions to state and county mental hospitals; 30% of psychiatric admissions to Veterans Administration hospitals; and about 20% of admissions to private psychiatric hospitals.

Schizophrenia is incurable. Its cause or causes are unknown, and it is impossible to predict what course the disease will take in any individual or what degree of recovery might be expected. There is even some disagreement about whether schizophrenia is a very old disease that has afflicted the human race throughout its history or a new disorder that appeared only in the last two or three centuries. To be sure, there are many theories about

In the 19th century, the insane were often imprisoned, as is shown in this lithograph of a Cairo, Egypt, prison in the 1820s. Imprisonment of the mentally ill has not yet, unfortunately, been eliminated worldwide.

schizophrenia's cause, its progression, and its eventual outcome. They are being explored by researchers around the world. For now, however, schizophrenia remains as mysterious as any ailment and the cause of extraordinary anguish to its victims and their loved ones.

FEATURES OF THE ILLNESS

The most prominent feature of schizophrenia is the profound disturbance in the way its victims view the world around them. They are in, but not of, the society in which they live. Their minds are divorced from reality. This estrangement is seen in every aspect of their thinking and emotions.

Schizophrenia's most dramatic symptoms (but not its most serious) are delusions and hallucinations. A delusion is a false belief or idea that logic and reason show to be "crazy." A hallucination is seeing, hearing, or sensing something that is not there. Both symptoms occur in other mental illnesses, but the content of the schizophrenic's delusions is often distinct enough that an experienced psychiatrist or clinical psychologist can readily identify the disorder. The untrained person cannot do so as easily. Once I was called from my desk by the receptionist at the newspaper where I then worked. I found a well-dressed woman in her mid-40s who pleaded for my help. The Federal Bureau of Investigation (FBI) had implanted electrodes in her brain and was listening to her every thought, she explained in a rising voice. She had complained to her hometown newspapers, to her congressman and two senators, and had written to the president of the United States. None of them had helped her. Of course, there was no help a medical writer could give except to suggest she talk with her physician or a psychiatrist.

Another common feature of schizophrenia is the disjointed conversation of its victims. Their discourse often consists of a series of vague statements strung together in an incoherent way. Listeners are left puzzled by what they have heard and perhaps wondering if they had missed something. To one degree or another, schizophrenics are often "flat" in mood. Their whole emotional outlook is deadened, and they show little or no warmth toward others. Even the most gruesome personal experience raises barely a flicker of anger, sadness, or grief. Prolonged immobility and jerky, robotlike movements are other common symptoms of the disorder. Typically, schizophrenics withdraw emotionally and even physically from the world and the people around them. They exclude reality and focus on their delusions, their hallucinations, and the other thoughts locked within the confines of their troubled minds.

For years psychiatrists regarded delusions and hallucinations as the hallmarks of schizophrenia. Today, less dramatic symptoms such as profound apathy, the inability to form a logical sentence, blunted emotions, and a much-reduced interest in social activity are considered the core of the disease. These symptoms also appear much harder to treat than delusions and hallucinations.

The bizarre thoughts and behavior of schizophrenia usually begin in late adolescence or early adulthood. The syndrome begins with a gradual deterioration of behavior that may be more noticeable to the patient's friends than to parents, especially in a high-school-age person. Schizophrenia occurs in equal numbers in males and females, but women, on average, develop the disease four or five years later than men. Rarely does schizophrenia first appear in either sex after age 40, and almost never after 50. Symptoms may occur suddenly and dramatically, but more often they begin slowly, almost imperceptibly. They grow more prolonged, more obvious, and more disturbing, almost inevitably ending in at least one hospitalization.

Schizophrenia exists among all races and cultures, and it is found in all countries. For decades, epidemiologists (disease specialists) have estimated that the disorder afflicted about 1% of the U.S. population. That estimate was upheld in 1984 by the National Institute of Mental Health (NIMH) in the most extensive assessment ever done of mental illnesses in the United States. The institute estimated that at any given time, .9% of the adult population suffered from schizophrenia.

At times, the insane delusions and hallucinations of a mind tinged by madness have captivated a mass of people, and the individual has been elevated by his or her followers to the status of prophet or savior. An example might be Adolf Hitler. Although it was never established definitively that he was clinically schizophrenic, much of his behavior and delusional thinking did resemble that of a paranoid schizophrenic. More often, the mentally ill have been ridiculed, demeaned, shunned, condemned as witches, and even burned alive because of accusations that their bodies were possessed by evil spirits.

Witches were often burned at the stake in medieval Europe. In some cases, these "witches" were merely schizophrenics whose actions sparked fears that they were possessed by demons.

THE HISTORY OF SCHIZOPHRENIA

Mental illness—madness, if you will—has been with us throughout recorded history. The Old Testament warns those inclined to break the Ten Commandments that "the Lord will smite you with madness and blindness and confusion of mind." The ancient Roman poet Horace (65–8 B.C.) wrote of a man who each day took a seat in an empty theater and enjoyed a performance no one else could see or hear, roundly applauding actors who existed

17

only in his mind. Much later, the English playwright William Shakespeare (1564–1616) drew heavily on the theme of the deranged mind for dramatic impact in such classics as *Macbeth*, *Hamlet*, and *King Lear*.

Schizophrenia was first categorized as a distinct mental illness late in the 19th century. However, for centuries before that, the deranged mind captured the attention of medical doctors. Hippocrates (460–357 B.C.), the ancient Greek known as the Father of Medicine, distinguished depression as a disease and also described several cases of manic-depression, the mental illness in which the deep lows of depression alternate with extreme highs in mood. Physicians, in their ancient and limited wisdom, tended to attribute disorders of the mind to defects in the body's humors, or fluids, or to organs that had wandered from their proper place.

During the Middle Ages, society's view of the mentally ill took on a more ominous tone. For centuries the medical theories had coexisted with what might be called religious or spiritual theories about mental disorders. Believers in these theories insisted that

Hippocrates, a Greek of the 5th century B.C., is considered the father of both Western and Middle Eastern medicine. Here he is depicted by an Arabian artist.

In the past, holy men performed exorcisms on schizophrenics in an effort to expel the devil from their bodies. Drawings such as this one suggest that schizophrenia has existed throughout human history.

the mentally ill were possessed by demons and devils. In the centuries following the Fall of Rome (A.D. 476), a period sometimes called the Dark Ages, scholars carefully listed what types of evil spirits caused what kinds of madness. In the Middle Ages and the early Renaissance, a series of incidents occurred in which mentally ill individuals who were believed to be possessed by demons were burned at the stake. The English used this punishment against Joan of Arc (1412–31). The French believed the voices she described hearing came from heaven and so followed

A milestone in psychiatric history occurred when the French doctor Philippe Pinel fought for, and won, more humane treatment of the mentally ill. Here he is seen unshackling a woman at the Salpetrière institution in Paris, about 1800.

her into battle against English troops. However, when the English captured her, the young woman known as the Maid of Orleans and later St. Joan was condemned as a witch and burned.

The first confinements of the mentally ill took place during the Middle Ages, beginning with what came to be known as the "ships of fools." The insane were loaded onto ships that sailed aimlessly from one European port to another. Starting in the 13th and 14th centuries, hospitals for the mentally disturbed were opened in several European countries, including France, Spain, and England. The word *bedlam*, meaning a scene of wild uproar and confusion, traces its origin to England's first insane asylum, Bethlehem Hospital in London. This institution was opened in about 1400.

A Modern Disease?

Schizophrenia was recognized as a separate type of mental illness by Emil Kraepelin, a German psychiatrist. After a careful study of people who had been hospitalized for mental disturbances and later released, Kraepelin described a distinct disorder in 1896 he called *dementia praecox*, a term meaning "early insanity." The name we use for the illness today, schizophrenia, was coined in 1911 by the Swiss psychiatrist Eugen Bleuler. He also contributed the idea that the truly distinctive feature of schizophrenics was a peculiar disturbance in the process through which they made mental associations. This disturbed thought process has been described as "a loosening of the links between thoughts." Schizophrenia, in literal translation, means "splitting of the mind," a phrase that led to the widely held misconception that the disorder involves a "split personality." It does not. The kind of disorder portrayed in popular writings and the films *The Three Faces of Eve* and *Sybil* is a far more rare psychiatric state called dissociative disorder. What schizophrenics suffer is not a split personality so much as no personality, in the sense that personality reflects a "human" feeling by which one person relates to another.

Most authorities believe schizophrenia has been present since the earliest days of the human race. Ancient writings seem to bear this out. For example, a study by 4 researchers at the NIMH uncovered descriptions of the delusions, hallucinations, and bizarre behavior that are typical of schizophrenia dating back more than 5,000 years. Although the sketchy descriptions are not proof positive, the researchers concluded that they do lend strong support to the idea that schizophrenia has existed throughout human history.

But an articulate minority of mental-health specialists contends schizophrenia is a disease of modern times. One of them, the American psychiatrist E. Fuller Torrey, argues that none of the ancient descriptions conclusively show schizophrenia. He believes it unlikely that any clear-cut case can be made for the disease's existence before the early 1800s. In 1809, two physicians, John Haslam in England and Philippe Pinel in France, wrote separate descriptions that, in Torrey's opinion, are the first unquestionable accounts of schizophrenia.

Evidence supports the idea that schizophrenia increased during the 1800s. Two theories about this evidence have emerged. First, the disorder had always existed but just was not recognized until the beginning of the 19th century. Thus, the increase is apparent rather than real. Second, schizophrenia is somehow a product of urbanization and the great social changes of the past two centuries. Both sides have their proponents and opponents. Unfortunately, the evidence does not exist to argue either theory very persuasively. And so we are left—as so often happens with questions about mental illness—to wonder.

Yet more than one of the recent treatments with chemical and social therapy offer hope that some schizophrenics can be cured. All of the evidence is not yet in, owing to the length of time and the complexity required for a thorough study of the many potential treatments, but the prospect for long-term sufferers of the ravages of schizophrenia seems to be brighter than it once was.

In the following pages you will learn more about schizophrenia and the mysteries that surround this terrible disorder. We will discuss how it affects its victims and their loved ones; whether schizophrenia is one disorder or more; what is known about its cause or causes; how genes and the environment may play separate but interconnected roles; what works and what does not in treating schizophrenics; and finally, whether all schizophrenics must have as bleak a future as they did in the past.

•   •   •   •

CHAPTER 2

. . . .

THE SCHIZOPHRENIC EXPERIENCE

Can I ever forget that I am schizophrenic? I am isolated and I am alone. I am never real. I play-act my life, touching and feeling only shadows. My heart and soul are touched, but the feelings remain locked away, festering inside me because they cannot find expression.

Can I ever forget that I am schizophrenic? Will I ever learn to live, to love unselfishly, to appropriate the beauties of life, to deny my hell and pain and darkness? Why is life like this? What have I done wrong? Have I created my own hell? If I did not create it, why was it inflicted upon me? What does it mean, all these weird feelings that shut me off from the rest of the world? Will they ever end?

Anonymous, *New York Times*, March 18, 1986

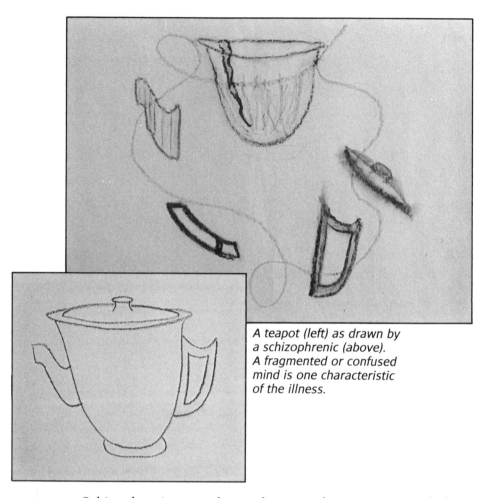

A teapot (left) as drawn by
a schizophrenic (above).
A fragmented or confused
mind is one characteristic
of the illness.

Schizophrenics say that unless you have experienced their mental illness, it is impossible to truly understand what suffering and anguish they have lived. But over the years, schizophrenics and those who have treated them have provided extraordinary accounts of the illness that give some sense of the disruption, confusion, distortions, and fear that are so much a part of the disease. Some of the symptoms of schizophrenia are evident only to a specialist, but others are evident to anyone. They can pose no problem or can be very harmful if not remedied.

The Symptoms: Delusions

Delusions and hallucinations are the symptoms the public most commonly associates with schizophrenia, although both occur in other mental illnesses and some schizophrenics never experience either. A delusion is a false belief that defies logic and common sense; it is divorced from the reality of the normal world. My wife vividly remembers a time in the 1970s when a tall man with a black beard, dressed in a frock coat and stovepipe hat, would walk through the U.S. Capitol in Washington, D.C., introducing himself solemnly and quite sincerely as Abraham Lincoln. It was not a sight or an experience people easily forgot. Such an incident may sound humorous. But what one never knows in such a casual encounter is what is going on inside the schizophrenic's mind or how the delusion may affect others. Norma MacDonald tried to convey some sense of her suffering in an article entitled "Living with Schizophrenia":

> I reached a stage where almost my entire world consisted
> of tortured contemplation of things which brought pain
> and unutterable depression. My brain, after a short time,
> became sore with a real physical soreness, as if it had been
> rubbed with sandpaper until it was raw. It felt like a bleed-
> ing sponge.

It is all but impossible for family or friends to talk a schizophrenic out of his or her delusion. To the person suffering the delusion, it is very real indeed. One schizophrenic believed she was living on Venus and stood on chairs and tables spouting gibberish, which presumably she thought was the language of the Venusians. Another schizophrenic felt she had the power to control the weather and the movement of the sun. Later she became convinced her youngest child would grow up to be mentally ill and that she must kill him to prevent his suffering.

A classic in the writings about schizophrenia is the book *Autobiography of a Schizophrenic Girl*, the story of a young French girl's struggle against mental illness, compiled by her psychiatrist, Marguerite Sechehaye. At one point, the girl, Renée, offers this glimpse into a schizophrenic's mind:

> I literally hated people, without knowing why. In dreams
> and frequently in waking fantasies I constructed an elec-
> tric machine to blow up the earth and everyone with it.
> But what was even worse, with the machine I would rob
> all men of their brains, thus creating robots obedient to
> my will alone. That was my greatest, most terrible revenge.

The delusions of schizophrenics often involve "knowing" they are being watched or that people can read their minds. It is very

This self-portrait by a paranoid schizophrenic reveals his tortured self-image. The face is hidden, protected, even semidisguised.

frightening and threatening to feel that every stranger they pass on the street knows their innermost thoughts and deepest secrets. Sometimes schizophrenics believe they can control the minds of others or that their brain is indiscriminately beaming their thoughts out to the world like a radio or television transmitter. Other common delusions include themes of persecution or of being attacked. Louise Wilson wrote of one such paranoid delusion in *This Stranger, My Son*, her account of life with a mentally ill child:

> He refused to touch any food that I had prepared or handled, even a bakery cake, if my hand had untied the string. Not until years later did we hear he was afraid his food was being poisoned.

The Symptoms: Hallucinations

The other most common symptom is hallucinations—hearing, seeing, or sensing something that is not there—which may or may not accompany the schizophrenic's delusions. Hallucinations usually begin with a heightened awareness of the senses. "Ordinary colors appeared to be much too bright, and sunlight seemed dazzling in intensity," one patient wrote in *The Inner World of Mental Illness*. This hypersensitivity of the senses may be followed by visual distortions. A small kitten may suddenly appear to become a snarling tiger. Renée, in *Autobiography of a Schizophrenic Girl*, recounted how she watched a stone jar decorated with blue flowers come alive, and then a chair and table.

Auditory hallucinations are the most common type in schizophrenia. A person may hear only a single voice, several, or many. They may be soft or loud, occasional or persistent. One patient told psychiatrist E. Fuller Torrey that her voices increased in volume whenever she turned on her television set—so much that she could not watch any program. Usually the voices vilify and curse the schizophrenic, telling him how wretched, evil, and terrible he is. They mock and taunt, issuing orders. Her voices commanded Renée to burn her right hand. Finally she complied, placing her hand on glowing fireplace coals. Only the unexpected arrival of her boss saved her from grave injury.

Visual hallucinations are much less common than the sound of voices that are not there. Again, these are often unpleasant, frequently including violence and destruction. Even rarer are hallucinations of smell, taste, and touch, which are also usually unpleasant. Putrid odors, often seemingly coming from within the person himself; strange tastes, with or without food or liquids in the mouth; sensations of pain with no cause, or insects biting or crawling on the flesh are examples reported by schizophrenics. An acute episode of schizophrenia, particularly its delusions and hallucinations, has been compared to a "bad trip" caused by psychedelic drugs. It is far worse, however, for the schizophrenic's break with reality goes on and on.

The Symptoms: Chaotic Speech

The thoughts and speech of a schizophrenic are disordered and disorganized. Conversations are marked by vague, disconnected statements that strike the average listener as irrational. Sometimes their discourse is so chaotic and unintelligible—a jumble of words and phrases psychiatrists call "word salad"—that diagnosing their condition is rather easy. At other times, the disjointed thought and speech patterns are more subtle. Such a conversation with a schizophrenic sounds difficult to follow but not bizarre—like talking with an expert about a subject you know only slightly. The individual sentences seem all right, but you just do not grasp what is being said. This "loosening of the links between thoughts" seen in schizophrenia is exhibited in the extreme in a diary kept by a patient during an acute schizophrenic episode. The man, a high school graduate of above-average intelligence, kept his diary during the two weeks his break with reality was at its most severe. It was published in *The Inner World of Mental Illness* and includes this passage:

> When you wish upon a star. red—stop amber—caution purple—be on look out Green—go ahead with what you are doing God help us to take advice from other people and show them we can take being talked about and not get mad or lose you temper How music grew bauer and Peyser At last Dr. Hughes I've come to my decision. I am ready to let people know by living more in reality and quite runing from myself. Because I a not a bably and more. but a man with God giving emotion's.

Other Evidence of Possible Illness

Delusions, hallucinations, and chaotic speech are glaring and readily recognized symptoms of a disturbed mind. Less dramatic but even more debilitating for the schizophrenic is a range of symptoms that include profound apathy, markedly blunted emotions, a lack of curiosity, and a complete loss of interest in ideas and social relations. Needless to say, being mildly depressed now and then is a condition most people endure, especially when in their teens. Such a feeling is not to be confused with the onset of schizophrenia, which only an expert can diagnose. These symptoms increase gradually in intensity until they dominate the schizophrenic's behavior. The person withdraws emotionally and often physically from the world. He will spend hours, even days, alone in a room, preoccupied with his bizarre, broken thoughts, his delusions and hallucinations. When walking on the street, he will avoid close friends and old acquaintances, pretending not to see them. The schizophrenic will refuse to initiate conversations or may not answer when someone speaks to him. "I had little or no desire to communicate with real people, although I talked extensively with an imaginary companion," one schizophrenic wrote. Norma MacDonald, an unusual schizophrenic who eventually recovered enough to become a psychiatric nurse, offered this observation:

> During my years as a psychiatric nurse, I have realized that I am not likely ever to know if my problems are shared by other schizophrenics or not, for the acutely ill are as much of a puzzle to me as they are to staff who have never known the illness. So incapable of communication, the schizophrenic cannot seem to make any of his needs or wishes clear. . . . Their fears and disturbances are familiar territory to me. I've been there. But when it comes to understanding what goes on in the patient's mind to cause the moods, then anyone's guess is as good as mine.

The most characteristic changes in schizophrenics are inappropriate expressions of emotion and what psychiatrists call "flattened" emotions. For example, a schizophrenic might suddenly start applauding during a funeral service while others' heads are bowed in silent prayer. Laughing uproariously or giggling at hearing sad news or crying sadly while reading a particularly funny passage in a novel are other examples of inappropriate emotions. One patient said his outbreaks of inappropriate be-

"Son of Sam" murderer David Berkowitz claimed that he heard voices telling him to kill. Hearing voices is common among schizophrenics.

havior resulted because his mind was occupied with half a dozen thoughts at the same time. He might be talking about something serious but burst out laughing at something funny that crossed his mind.

The flattening of emotions among schizophrenics is by far the most striking change. Anger, rage, love, hate, indignation, sadness, and joy all seem to diminish, leaving a pitiful, emotionless shell of a human. Psychiatrist Solomon H. Snyder has described his chilling encounter with one such schizophrenic in *The Troubled Mind: A Guide to Release from Distress*.

> I have seen a patient describe in vivid detail how his mother was struck and killed by a car in front of his eyes, how he went over to the body and noticed that there was blood spurting from her throat, and how one of her legs was completely detached from the rest of the body. He described all of this and the events of the subsequent weeks including the funeral and family disruption without the faintest indication of strong emotion. Through it all his story rambled on in a dry monotone.

Living in Hell

Some schizophrenics profess to have gained something from their illness. Norma MacDonald called her schizophrenia "living in hell" but added, "[I]t seems to lead to a deeper understanding of people and liking for people, and it's an exciting life, like being an explorer in a territory where no one else has ever been." Another woman described her first break with reality as "a time of inspiration and renewal."

But few would argue that the benefits gained from their illness were worth the pain and suffering they experienced. Esso Leete summed up her sense of loss.

> I am haunted by an evasive picture of what my life could have been, whom I might have become, what I might have accomplished. My schizophrenia is a sad realization, a painful reality, that I live with every day. I wonder what, if anything, I could have done differently either to avoid developing schizophrenia or to lessen its severity.

•   •   •   •

CHAPTER 3

· · · · · · · · · · · · · · · · · ·

ONE DISEASE OR MANY?

Lecture on schizophrenia, late 1800s

Not all schizophrenics suffer the same illness. Most mental-health experts believe that what we call schizophrenia is actually a series of disorders that display similar symptoms. Eugen Bleuler certainly believed so. He titled his classic 1911 book on the subject *Dementia Praecox or the Group of Schizophrenias*.

Over the years, attempts have been made to divide and cate-gorize schizophrenia into various subgroups. Knowing one type of schizophrenia from another would be helpful in diagnosing patients, in helping researchers better understand the causes of the disorders, and in learning what treatments work best in what

SUBTYPES OF SCHIZOPHRENIA
(Most patients display two or three varieties)

Subtype	Symptoms	Comments
Paranoia (paranoid psychosis)	Delusions of grandeur or persecution, often by a large organization like the FBI	Occurs among older and more intelligent victims. Delusions can dominate life if not treated. (Not every paranoic is a true schizophrenic)
Hebephrenia	Clownish or absurd outbursts Gradual decrease in social contact	Patient seems to be playing like a child in some episodes, though no adult mental functions have actually been lost
Catatonia	Extreme muscle tension "Waxy flexibility" Robot-like movements or Frenzied, even lethal motion	More treatable with drugs than other subtypes. Frenzy can lead to death by exhaustion if not stopped.

All patients can become depressed during the recovery period after an attack, especially if the episode was a severe or prolonged one.

form of the disease. Unfortunately, such efforts have proved completely unsuccessful. Indeed, it is not even known whether some people suffer but a mild form of schizophrenia—one that is less severe and escapes detection.

The Problem of Diagnosis

No objective way exists to diagnose schizophrenia. No chemicals in the blood, the brain, or the spinal fluid are known to indicate its presence. Neither X rays nor the examination of cells under the microscope can reveal whether a person suffers the disorder. So psychiatrists must rely on symptoms to guide them in deciding whether a person suffers from schizophrenia. Unfortunately, a number of diseases may have the same symptoms.

In the United States, the requirements for diagnosing someone as schizophrenic are laid out in the third edition of the *Diagnostic and Statistical Manual of Mental Disorders* (DSM III), published in 1980. This book, which physicians and clinical psychologists rely on in diagnosing mental illnesses, is the official diagnostic system of the American Psychiatric Association. The diagnosis of schizophrenia includes a list of specific symptoms, at least one of which must have been present for no less than six months. If a person does not meet the strict criteria in DSM III, it is improper to label him or her schizophrenic.

The Three Subtypes

In the late 1800s, what we now call schizophrenia was considered three distinct mental diseases, whose symptoms are listed in the table. Paranoid psychosis was described in 1868. Three years later, hebephrenia was reported, then catatonia in 1874. In 1896, Emil Kraepelin realized that these three disorders were far more alike than they were different. He grouped them together as dementia praecox, or "early insanity," to indicate their early age of onset. Since that time, the three disorders have continued to serve as a subgrouping of schizophrenia.

As diagnostic methods improved, new categories of mental illness were defined. These photographs of persons who attempted suicide or murder of their own children were used to classify types of insanity.

A catatonic schizo-phrenic may remain frozen in one position for hours. Although they appear to be oblivious to their surroundings, they do continue to absorb some of what goes on around them.

Catatonia Catatonic schizophrenia also derives its name from the Greek. (*Catatonia* means tension.) The most memorable symptom of catatonic schizophrenia is the extraordinary changes in the tension of a catatonic's voluntary muscles—those muscles humans can control by their own will. Catatonics may assume a position of almost complete immobility, or they may race about in frenzied excitement. Sometimes they alternate one state with the other.

During a catatonic stupor, a person may assume a statuesque pose and remain fixed in it for hours, with limbs appearing to defy exhaustion or even gravity. The face is expressionless, and the person remains speechless, as if the brain had fled from all worldly contact. If someone repositions the arm or leg of a schizophrenic in such a trance, the limb will remain as placed—a phenomenon called "waxy flexibility." At other times, catatonic schizophrenics move their body as if they were robots responding to programmed commands. Catatonics may refuse to eat—even to the point of death—and some lose or give up control of their bowels and bladder. While people in catatonic trances may appear divorced from all contact with the world, they often do take in, for later consideration, what is going on around them. It is not unusual for doctors, nurses, and attendants who have made remarks while a catatonic schizophrenic was in a trance to find themselves hearing their own words repeated by the patient weeks or months later.

Rapid and excited motion is the other extreme in the behavior of catatonic schizophrenics. They may race wildly about—scream, cry, laugh, or sing loudly, and bang on walls or floors. Their actions are frenzied, even lethal. Some people have actually died from exhaustion and heart failure as a result of their frantic activities.

Hebephrenia Hebephrenic, or disorganized, schizophrenia describes patients whose behavior is childish, silly, and entirely inappropriate. The name itself comes from ancient Greek mythology. Hebe was the cupbearer to the gods who, as she made her rounds, overindulged in the wine she carried. As a result, Hebe was always giggling and acting the clown. Hebephrenics follow this pattern of absurd behavior—giggling, grimacing, making faces in the mirror, spouting nonsensical rhymes, or peeking around corners like a playful child. This type of schizophrenia comes on slowly and is marked by a gradual decrease in social activities and contacts. Delusions and hallucinations do occur, but they are not major features of the hebephrenic's illness.

Paranoia Paranoid schizophrenics are plagued by delusions of persecution or grandeur, usually both, and often suffer hallucinations. Typically, these symptoms are accompanied by anxiety, anger, argumentativeness, and sometimes violent behavior. Paranoid schizophrenia usually occurs a little later in life than either hebephrenic or catatonic schizophrenia. Its victims tend to be not only older but more intelligent and more alert than hebephrenics or catatonics.

Although many people feel persecuted at times (and some actually are), the persecution delusions of paranoid schizophrenics truly dominate their lives. They are certain that someone is "out to get them," and they will often detail extensive "evidence" to prove it. At some time or another, most schizophrenics have delusions that someone is after them. But these are vague and undefined forebodings. Paranoid schizophrenics, on the other hand, are very specific about who is after them and why. The persecutors in their vivid delusions are frequently powerful government institutions—the FBI, the Central Intelligence Agency (CIA), the Pentagon, the White House, or even beings from another planet.

People who fit into this subtype may be consumed with delusions of their own great importance. Thus, we find some introducing themselves as Jesus Christ, the Virgin Mary, Abraham Lincoln, Napoleon Bonaparte, Julius Caesar, or Cleopatra, and often dressing the part. Others proclaim they bear messages of grave import, new revelations from God, a plan that will create world peace, or one that will save the nation from communism.

Not everyone who suffers from paranoia is schizophrenic. DSM III now limits that diagnosis to paranoid individuals who suffer fully developed schizophrenia. Less severe types of paranoid behavior are assigned other names, such as paranoid disorder, paranoia, or paranoid personality disorder.

Of all the disorders, paranoid schizophrenia is probably the most devastating. Indeed, some researchers believe that it is not

The delusions that sometimes characterize schizophrenia may lead the victim to think he or she is of great importance. This painting by Goya shows mental patients acting out their fantasies.

a true schizophrenia. They argue it should be classified along with the other paranoid disorders as a separate group of mental illnesses.

These categories of schizophrenia—hebephrenia, catatonia, and paranoia—all sound fairly neat and precise. Unfortunately, most schizophrenics display a mixture of symptoms from two or all three categories. Moreover, symptoms tend to change over time. A person who seems to be a catatonic schizophrenic when first diagnosed may shift over a few years' time and display symptoms of hebephrenia. Even the psychiatrists' rule "Once a paranoid always a paranoid" is not ironclad. Today, most schizophrenics are designated as suffering undifferentiated schizophrenia. This simply means that the patient's symptoms represent a mixture of those seen in hebephrenics, catatonics, and paranoids.

Schizophrenialike Behavior

A number of people, although not truly schizophrenic, suffer ailments that include schizophrenialike symptoms. These disorders, which are described below, include schizo-affective psychosis, schizophreniform illness, brief reactive psychosis, and schizophrenialike behavior related to drug abuse, giving birth, and organic diseases of the brain.

Often schizophrenics become depressed as they recover from an acute attack of their disease, perhaps because their mind once again allows them to grasp the severity of their illness. There is another group of patients who seem to suffer a combination of both depression and schizophrenia called schizo-affective psychosis, an illness distinct from schizophrenia. Generally, it is regarded as more akin to manic-depression. For one thing, schizo-affectives are more likely to recover than people with full-blown schizophrenia.

A diagnosis of schizo-affective psychosis requires that the symptoms of depression or mania occur before or at the same time as those of schizophrenia begin. Beyond that, there is little agreement. The affective illnesses—depression and manic-depression—are in their pure forms rather easy to distinguish from schizophrenia. Essentially, the affective illnesses involve changes in mood. That is, a patient experiences very high or very low periods during his illness. Schizophrenia, on the other hand, affects thought more than mood, which does not mean that schizophrenics do not suffer ups and downs in mood or that bizarre thoughts never trouble manics and depressives. They do. Indeed, many patients exhibit a confusing array of symptoms from both diseases, making their illness more difficult to diagnosis. Even the DSM III acknowledges that "at the present time there is no consensus on how this category should be defined."

Schizophreniform illness—the name means "looks like schizophrenia"—is not considered true schizophrenia, although the symptoms of the disease are present. The disorder is present if schizophrenic symptoms last less than six months but more than a week or two. As with schizo-affective psychosis, the chances for recovery from schizophreniform illness are much greater than from schizophrenia. About one in three schizophreniforms experience one episode and never suffer schizophrenic symptoms again. Others, however, go through a cyclic pattern of illness similar to that often seen in the affective disorders. They suffer bouts of schizophreniform illness separated by periods when they appear perfectly normal. Still others eventually go on from schizophreniform illness to true schizophrenia.

The families of schizophreniform patients have a high incidence of manic-depression but a low incidence of true schizophrenia. This fact seems to be further evidence that the lesser illness only mimics schizophrenia and is usually not as serious.

Occasionally, an individual who is otherwise perfectly normal will suffer what is called brief reactive psychosis, a short period in which he exhibits some symptoms of schizophrenia. Delusions and hallucinations usually occur in brief reactive psychosis; bizarre thought patterns are much less common. The symptoms strike suddenly, last only a few days, and then stop as suddenly as they began. Most people recover from such episodes and never suffer another. Overwhelming stress appears to play a role in some cases—soldiers in combat, for example, or someone stranded and struggling for survival in extreme heat or cold—but the underlying cause of these brief breaks with reality remains a mystery. In spite of their symptoms, such people are not schizophrenic.

Equally baffling are the cases of women who suffer schizophrenialike symptoms after childbirth. Although it is not uncommon for a new mother to suffer some depression following delivery of her baby, about 1 woman in 1,000 suddenly develops signs of schizophrenia 3 to 7 days after giving birth. Again, delusions and hallucinations are most often seen. The mother may swear that

People may show schizophrenialike symptoms, called brief reactive psychosis, in periods of great stress such as wartime. Most such episodes never recur, and their cause is unknown.

her baby has been kidnapped, that someone else's infant has been substituted for her own, or that her healthy offspring has some terrible deformity. Some hear voices telling them the baby is abnormal or evil and even commands to kill the infant. Drugs normally prescribed to fight severe depression usually bring recovery within two weeks in these women. But during the mother's illness, the baby is separated from her for its own protection.

What triggers these symptoms is unknown. Psychological theories suggesting that delusions and hallucinations stem from the mother's ambivalent feelings about her child were once widely accepted. Today, biology is the prime suspect. A leading theory suggests that the enormous changes in a woman's hormones that occur during and after giving birth are somehow responsible. Again, such symptoms do not represent actual schizophrenia. Most women recover with no future problems. Some do end up becoming schizophrenic, but experts believe that these women would have developed the disease even if they had never given birth.

A few physical diseases that affect the brain may result in symptoms that mimic schizophrenia. These include brain tumors and certain infections of the brain. Physicians must therefore gather a good medical history and test patients for other possible disorders before diagnosing them as schizophrenics.

The Drug Connection

Psychoactive drugs, which affect the brain's mental powers, can also trigger schizophrenialike symptoms. Hospital emergency rooms have seen sharp increases in such cases with the epidemic of drug abuse that has afflicted the nation over the past several decades. Amphetamines ("speed") can produce a psychotic break with reality that closely resembles acute schizophrenia. Cocaine, in addition to its potentially lethal effects on the heart and lungs, may cause behavior similar to paranoid schizophrenia. From the psychiatric point of view, amphetamines and cocaine act in much the same way in the brain by enhancing the effects of a chemical that is linked to schizophrenia. Users of lysergic acid diethylamide (LSD) and phencyclidine (PCP, or "angel dust") may suddenly suffer from delusions, hallucinations, and bizarre thinking. Even marijuana, which too many people regard as essentially harmless, will produce a paranoid state in a few users.

Drug abuse can destroy the body and seriously damage the brain. No doubt exists about that. But to date, no good evidence has been found that psychoactive drugs can cause true schizophrenia.

Drugs do, however, provide a clue about exactly how the mind works, or does not work, when it is altered by chemical stimuli. A better knowledge of schizophrenia could be had if we understood how the mind functions with and without those chemicals.

•   •   •   •   •

CHAPTER 4

BIOLOGICAL ASPECTS

Drawing by a 25-year-old schizophrenic

In spite of years of effort, no one can yet say what first goes wrong in schizophrenia or what is its underlying cause. That is not to say that nothing has been learned. It now appears that schizophrenia is an extraordinarily complex disorder whose basic mechanisms, biological and environmental, are likely to take many years to understand.

One constant in the pathology of schizophrenia is that about one per-cent of the population will be affected by the disease.

Schizophrenia runs in families, a fact that is now well established. On average, 1 person out of 100 persons will suffer schizophrenia. Among children who have either a schizophrenic mother or a schizophrenic father, about 10 out of 100 will develop the disease. Moreover, studies show that almost half the children who have two schizophrenic parents go on to develop schizophrenia themselves. A broader finding is that 10 to 15% of the immediate family of schizophrenics (including parents, siblings, or children) suffer from the disorder.

That schizophrenia runs in families suggests that the disorder is inherited. But it could also mean that people who suffer schizophrenia raise their children in a way that greatly increases their offspring's chances of becoming schizophrenic. This is known as the "nature-nurture" controversy—whether schizophrenia is caused by people's genes or by their environment. It is a question that has sparked lively debates and heated arguments for decades. It seems clear that the causes of schizophrenia include more than just a variety of abnormal social and psychological events, which was an idea long popular with many psychiatrists and psychologists. The vast majority of mental-health experts now believe both genetic (biologic) and environmental factors play a role in schizophrenia, but determining the precise contribution of either factor in schizophrenia is a tremendous challenge. More researchers are accepting the challenge each year.

When we inherit something in our physical makeup from our parents, we do so through our genes. Each cell in our body contains some 6 million genes, arranged on 46 rodlike structures called chromosomes. Genes, bits of material on chromosomes, determine such inherited traits as our hair and eye color, the

The most important indication that schizophrenia has biological roots is that the disease often runs in families.

upper limits of our height and intelligence, and whether we produce too much, too little, or just the right amounts of the enzymes, hormones, and other substances the body needs. Half of the genes come from the mother, the other half from the father. Genes determine how well or poorly we respond to certain drugs and the way we are affected by many environmental pollutants. Inheriting a certain gene or genes will cause specific, sometimes fatal, diseases or make us susceptible to others if we encounter certain things in the environment. Hay fever is one example of an inherited vulnerability. People born with that predisposition develop allergies only if they inhale enough environmental substances—such as mold spores and tree and grass pollens. Schizophrenia is now regarded as a disease in which a predisposition—not the disorder itself—is inherited.

Studies Involving Twins

The strongest evidence that genes are important in schizophrenia comes from studies of twins and adopted children. Twins are either identical or fraternal. Identical twins are produced from a single egg that splits after it has been fertilized. As a result, they are genetically identical; they share exactly the same genes. In contrast, fraternal twins result from the fertilization of two separate eggs. About half the genes of fraternal twins are alike; the other half are different. Fraternal twins have no more in common genetically with each other than they do with any other child born to the same mother and father. This difference is important. If schizophrenia is indeed inherited, it should strike both members of a set of identical twins more often than it does both members of a set a fraternal twins.

And this is what happens. Studies of identical twins reveal that if one twin develops schizophrenia, his or her identical twin also develops the mental illness 35 to 60% of the time. This rather large range—from 35 to 60%—results in part because the twins studies used different standards for deciding at what point each twin was schizophrenic. Studies that have followed identical twins over many years show that the chances of both twins becoming schizophrenic increase as they grow older. Among fraternal twins, studies show the concordance for schizophrenia—the existence of schizophrenia in both twins—is only 10 to 15% (this is the same figure as for nontwin siblings). Thus, the likelihood that both identical twins will suffer the disorder is two to four times

Studies of twins have shown a high concordance of schizophrenia in both individuals. But one twin's illness is not a guarantee that the other will fall sick, too, suggesting that some other factors also play a role.

greater than for both fraternal twins. Moreover, when one of two identical twins suffers schizophrenia, then a child born to either one of the twins, affected or not, has a 13% risk of suffering schizophrenia. This suggests that both identical twins passed on the same genetic risk to their offspring, whether or not the twin actually suffers from schizophrenia.

Clearly, the twin studies show that schizophrenia runs in families. Nonetheless, these studies did not win over everyone to the view that genes play a role in the disease. Some critics argued that identicial twins are raised more identically than fraternal twins. Identical twins, for example, are often extremely hard to tell apart. Fraternal twins usually look quite different, and they may be both boys, both girls, or one of each sex. If identical twins are treated more alike then fraternal twins, the argument went, then this difference could explain the difference in schizophrenia rates between identical and fraternal twins.

Studies Involving Adoption

Studies of identical twins raised away from each other and of adopted children who had at least one schizophrenic natural parent have demolished the nurture argument. They show that these children are as likely to develop schizophrenia as they would be if they were raised by their natural parents. Consider the situation of identical twins raised in separate households without any knowledge of one another. If one develops schizophrenia, the chances are about 50–50 the other will become schizophrenic. So the odds are the same, whether identical twins are raised together or apart.

Adoption studies have shed further light on whether schizophrenia is inherited. In the United States, a team of researchers looked at two groups of adults. Each of the adults had been separated from his or her mother within a few days after birth and raised without ever seeing her again or having any contact with her family. One group of 47 was made up of people whose mothers had been schizophrenics. The mothers of the 50 people in the other group did not suffer the illness. The researchers

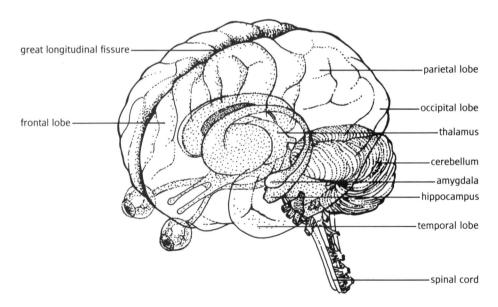

Some studies indicate that the brain's emotion center, the limbic system (which includes the hippocampus and amygdala), is smaller in a schizophrenic than in a normal brain.

discovered that 5 of the 97 people in the study were schizophrenic, and all 5 were born to mothers who suffered schizophrenia. Several adoption studies in Denmark add further support. They show that adopted children who had a schizophrenic natural parent are at far higher risk of developing the mental disorder than adopted children who did not.

Finally, what happens if a child with no family history of schizophrenia is adopted into a family in which someone is schizophrenic? Researchers have found that such a child has no greater danger of developing schizophrenia than if he or she had been adopted by a normal family. Such studies have now settled the question of whether genetics plays some role in schizophrenia. It seems quite clear that it does, but that identical twins do not have 100% concordance for schizophrenia means that more than genetics is involved in the disease. Schizophrenia does not fit the classic patterns of dominant inheritance (whereby the disease occurs even if only one parent passes on the gene) or recessive inheritance. (The defective gene must be received from both parents.) Today, most mental-health experts believe that what is inherited is a *tendency* to the disease. Before schizophrenia actually develops, other events must occur. Just what these environmental influences might be is a hotly debated issue that will be discussed in the next chapter.

The Brain's Role

During the 19th and 20th centuries, a variety of structural abnormalities were found in the brains of many deceased schizophrenics. Over the last two decades, remarkable new devices with names such as computerized axial tomography (the CAT scan) and magnetic resonance imaging (for analyzing the chemistry of the brain) have allowed scientists to study the brains of living humans, including schizophrenics. These, too, have revealed evidence of a number of abnormalities. Such abnormalities may or may not be genetically determined, and none have been linked unquestionably to schizophrenia. Their role in the disease, if any, remains as much a matter of conjecture now as in 1809 when John Haslam in England reported the first autopsy studies on the brains of schizophrenics. Yet they are clues, and scientists are trying hard to understand them. As in any mystery, no one knows just which clues will lead to the solution.

The brain consists of two hemispheres whose structures mirror each other. Both autopsy and living-brain examinations have found differences between these two hemispheres in schizophrenics, differences not found in nonschizophrenics. For example, one study reported that some schizophrenics had a higher than normal level of dopamine in the left side of the brain but not in the right side. Dopamine is one of many chemicals called neurotransmitters that nerve cells use to transmit messages. It is suspected of playing an important role in schizophrenia. A number of other differences have been noted in the brains of schizophrenics—some differences exist between the physical structures of the brain's two hemispheres, some in the chemical activities that occur on each side.

A remarkable and unexplained finding came when researchers at the University of California, Los Angeles (UCLA), examined the brains of 10 chronic schizophrenics and 8 nonschizophrenics who died between ages 25 and 67. The problem lay in a group of nerve cells called pyramidal cells, situated in a part of the brain called the hippocampus, where many emotions are governed. The scientists discovered that the pyramidal cells were dramatically disorganized in the schizophrenics but not in the normal individuals. The reason for the disarrayed cells is unknown, but the UCLA team suggested the problem probably occurred late in the first trimester of the person's development in the mother's womb, a time when cells in the fetus normally align themselves in an orderly manner in the process of forming the hippocampus.

Study of the living brain has also revealed other intriguing differences between schizophrenics and nonschizophrenics. Studies now suggest that the whole-brain metabolism of schizophrenics—the overall total of chemical reactions in their brains—is lower than normal. Several studies, but not all, have found a reduced blood flow to the frontal and prefrontal cortex in some schizophrenics. These two regions play a role in the brain's higher mental functions.

Among the oldest and most consistent findings is that many schizophrenics have enlarged ventricles in their brain. The ventricles are a series of connected cavities that the cerebrospinal fluid flows through. This colorless liquid surrounds the brain and the spinal cord, helping to cushion it against injury from sudden blows. Enlarged ventricles indicate some shrinkage of adjacent

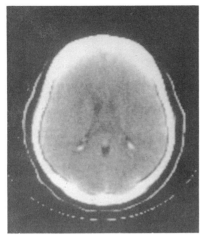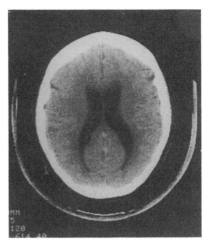

CAT scan of a schizophrenic's brain (left) and of a normal brain, viewed from above. Enlarged ventricles, which cause pressure on the adjacent tissue, are the clearest evidence of a difference between the two brains.

brain tissue, usually leading to deterioration of that tissue. The studies vary considerably, however, in what percentage of schizophrenics have enlarged ventricles. Moreover, some researchers report they can find no significant difference in ventricle size between individuals with the disease and those without it.

Other studies have found that the brains of schizophrenics weigh less than those of people who are normal. Recent evidence even suggests that specific parts of the brain are smaller in schizophrenics. These include the limbic system (a group of structures in the midbrain involved in such feelings as joy, sadness, fear, anger, and sexual arousal) and, particularly, two key centers of the emotions, the hippocampus and the amygdala. Several studies have also shown that schizophrenics tend to have a smaller cerebellar vermis, a part of the brain involved in the control of coordination. What is unclear is whether these apparent size differences might be due to the failure of the brain to develop properly or if they might result from the death of cells at some later time.

Clearly, the brains of many schizophrenics contain abnormal structures or are unusual in their chemical functioning. What remains unclear is how any of these differences causes either the illness itself or its symptoms. Moreover, if brain abnormalities are always present—as, for example, the disorganized pyramidal cells of the hippocampus surely are—then why is schizophrenia

49

often an episodic disease, occurring periodically? Why are episodes of acute severity interspersed with less serious periods? That key question, too, remains unanswered.

Current Theories on the Brain's Role A number of biological theories have been advanced to explain schizophrenia. One notion popular with the public blames nutritional deficiencies. Supporters of this "orthomolecular" theory urge treatment with large doses of vitamins, including B12, C, E, thiamine, and folic acid, as well as such minerals as zinc and manganese. The therapy also restricts consumption of carbohydrates, caffeine, and alcohol. Almost all physicians reject this megavitamin and diet approach because experimental studies have failed to show its value. Nevertheless, megavitamins are strongly backed by the American Schizophrenia Association, a group made up largely of schizophrenics and their families.

Currently, the most hotly pursued biological theory of schizophrenia involves the neurotransmitter dopamine. Some researchers also have renewed their interest in the idea that viral infections within the brain may contribute to the illness.

Several neurotransmitters are suspected of perhaps playing some role in schizophrenia. Serotonin and norepinephrine are two likely candidates. But the evidence implicating dopamine is by far the strongest. Consider these facts. First, high doses of amphetamines can trigger severe schizphrenialike symptoms, and amphetamines increase the levels of dopamine in the brain. Second, the drug L-dopa, used to treat the disabling ailment Parkinson's disease, increases the brain's output of dopamine. When L-dopa is given to schizophrenics, their condition gets worse. Third, all the drugs used to treat schizophrenia interfere with dopamine.

Intriguing as these facts are, years of research have failed to pinpoint what role dopamine may play in schizophrenia. Initially, some experts believed that an excess of dopamine was the culprit. Others suggested that the problem might be an inadequate supply of monoamine oxidase (MAO). This enzyme breaks down dopamine, and if not enough MAO were available, excessive amounts of dopamine would build up in the brain. However, it is clear now that schizophrenia is more complicated than too much dopamine in the brain.

Some findings by researchers at Johns Hopkins University in Baltimore suggest that the disease may result from a particular hypersensitivity to normal or near normal amounts of dopamine. They found that living schizophrenics had a greater than normal number of dopamine receptors in their brains. Receptors are molecules on the surface of cells that a chemical must attach to before it can have any effect on the cell. The more dopamine receptors, the stronger the effect of the chemical. The schizophrenics had excessive receptors whether they had been treated with drugs for their illness or not. This finding was important because it meant the drug treatments were not the cause of the receptor increase. Perhaps, then, it is this excess of receptors that explains dopamine's role in schizophrenia.

And perhaps not. Over a century ago, scientists began searching for a "toxin" that caused schizophrenia. Ever since, efforts to find some purely chemical cause of the disease have proved frustratingly unsuccessful. If excessive dopamine receptors are the key and are always present, then the question must again be asked, Why is schizophrenia episodic? Yet the evidence implicating dopamine is so strong that most brain researchers remain convinced it must play an important role in the disease, even if it is not the direct cause.

The idea that infections might cause schizophrenia dates back to the early years of the 20th century. Since then, researchers have shown sporadic interest in the theory. For one thing, 54% of schizophrenics are born in the winter and spring, months

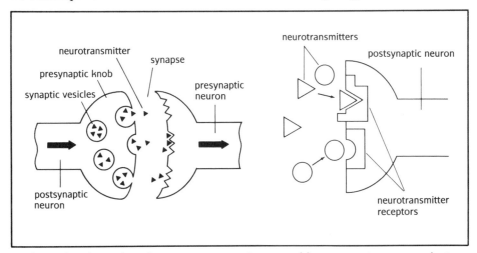

These drawings show how neurotransmitters enable neurons to communicate with each other. The neurotransmitter dopamine is thought to play a role in schizophrenia.

when infections occur more often. And it is known that viruses can attack the brain and that slow-acting viruses can remain inactive for years before suddenly beginning to multiply and cause illness. One theory suggests that a slow-acting virus infects the fetus in the womb and that this infection causes changes in the brain that lead to schizophrenia in adolescence or early adulthood.

What has sparked renewed interest in the infection theory is that some researchers believe schizophrenia resembles an autoimmune disease. An autoimmune disease is an illness in which the immune system—the body's natural defenses against disease—mistakenly attacks a person's own cells. In some schizophrenics there are found antibodies, killer proteins of the immune system, that can attack cells in the brain. Yet as intriguing as these and other findings are, the evidence that would link any viral infection to the cause of schizophrenia remains weak.

Scientists have no answer to the most fundamental question about schizophrenia: What is its cause? They can only hope the remarkable new research techniques and devices now available will eventually allow them to solve this puzzle. Some of the most promising of these new techniques are in the fields of psychology and psychiatry.

•   •   •   •

CHAPTER 5

· · · · · · · · · · · · · ·

PSYCHOLOGICAL ASPECTS

On Karl Johan Street by Edvard Munch

I n 1911, the year Eugen Bleuler gave the word *schizophrenia* to the world, Sigmund Freud published his theoretical explanation of the illness. Freud was a towering figure in psychiatry, an Austrian physician who became known as the Father of Psychoanalysis. Freud's underlying theory was that the key to mental disorders lies in the unconscious mind. There are still many adherents to this theory. He viewed repressed sexual feelings and conflicts as major factors in mental illness. In treatment, the psychoanalyst helps patients try to identify their repressed conflicts so they can use their insights and understandings to change their abnormal behavior.

Sigmund Freud (front left) and Carl Jung (front right) at Clark University, Worcester, Massachusetts, in 1908. The two were leading theorists in modern psychology.

Freud, however, had seen few schizophrenics in his practice. Indeed, his 1911 analysis of paranoid schizophrenia was based on the biographical account written by Daniel Schreber of his own mental illness, which had been published in 1903. Freud never examined Schreber; he never discussed Schreber's illness or family history with him. Nonetheless, based on the written account, Freud concluded that as a young child Schreber had been troubled by a conflict over "unconscious homosexuality." This, in turn, led to a reverse Oedipus complex. The Oedipus complex is a Freudian concept. It posits that young boys go through a stage in which they form a sexual attachment to their mothers, see their fathers as rivals, and want their fathers dead. However, according to Freud's interpretation, Schreber became attached to his father instead of his mother. And this led to Schreber's schizophrenia. Such a sweeping analysis of a major mental illness without personal contact with the patient would not be accepted by physicians and scientists today. Yet so great was Freud's overall contribution to psychiatry that his psychoanalytic view of schizophrenia was extraordinarily influential for decades.

Freud's explanation provoked some lively debates among his followers as they expanded the theory. Two of his most brilliant followers, Karl Abraham and Carl Jung, created a major split within the Freudian ranks. Abraham attributed schizophrenia to a blockage of the libido, a person's sexual desire and sexual drive. Jung blamed a chemical toxin. Freud joined the fray and supported Abraham. This and other differences caused Jung to reject many of Freud's teachings. Jung proposed his own psychiatric theories, based on his belief that there exists a collective unconscious of all mankind.

When Does Schizophrenia Start?

The Freudians battled among themselves in deciding at precisely what point psychological damage that eventually led to schizophrenia took place. Some argued it occurred in the womb before birth, or as one wrote, in "the unceasing terror and tension of

Today, parents are rarely thought to be responsible for causing schizophrenia in their children.

the fetal night." Others proposed that it developed in various stages during infancy and young childhood. They also argued whether Abraham was right in saying that schizophrenia sprang from inadequate libido development or whether it arose from poor ego development—from one's subconscious ability to recognize one's "self" from others. What almost all the Freudians did agree on was that the psychic injury causing schizophrenia stemmed from abnormal child-parent relationships. One common theme was parental rejection, which led to the now largely discredited concept of the "schizophrenigenic," or schizophrenia-causing, parent.

Certain personality traits in parents were blamed for schizophrenia in their offspring. Schizophrenigenic mothers were said to be cold, rejecting, insecure, aggressive, domineering, and often mentally ill themselves. Schizophrenia-causing fathers were described as inadequate males—passive, unaggressive in their dealings with others, and indifferent to their children. It is true that researchers find disturbed relationships within families when one member is schizophrenic, but no one has proved that they are the cause of the illness despite the possibility that genetics is involved; they could just as well be an effect of the disease. Disturbed communications could result because the child destined to become schizophrenic acts in a strange and disruptive manner long before the disorder's well-defined symptoms appear.

Today, mothers and fathers are blamed far less for causing schizophrenia in their offspring, which has helped reduce recriminations and anger within the families of schizophrenics. Parents often feel tremendous guilt, thinking that they are somehow personally to blame for the illness.

Halfway through the 20th century, the view that the cause of schizophrenia was skewed interactions within a family—rather than a parent directly—began to attract considerable attention. One research team studied the relationships in several families with a schizophrenic child and concluded that not a single marriage seemed normal or healthy. Communications became a key theme. How did family members communicate? What schizophrenia-causing messages were passed unconsciously from parent to child? The so-called double-bind theory of Gregory Bateson emerged as the best-known example of this concept. In *Surviving Schizophrenia: A Family Manual*, psychiatrist E. Fuller Torrey explained Bateson's concept:

Though recent studies have failed to prove that the stress of urban living contributes to the onset of schizophrenia, environmental factors do probably play a role in many mental illnesses.

According to this theory, schizophrenia results when children are put into an impossible heads-I-win-tails-you-lose situation. For example, a mother buys her son two ties for his birthday. He comes downstairs wearing one of the ties the next morning and his mother asks, "What's the matter, dear, don't you like the other tie I gave you?"

What Stress Can Do

The notion that schizophrenia is caused by an inability to cope with the psychological stresses of human existence is particularly popular with the general public. Schizophrenics and recovered schizophrenics frequently cite family pressures, job pressures, financial pressures, and the pressures of simply living as the cause of their break with reality. Stress, in a psychological sense, is any pressure that a person finds difficult to cope with. What one person might consider a challenge—finishing a 15-page term paper, for example—another will consider a high-stress situation. Stress is in the mind's eye of the beholder, not in the actual situation itself.

It is true that researchers find increasingly that stressful events can play a significant role in mental and physical ailments. We noted earlier that overwhelming stress, such as combat conditions, can bring on brief reactive psychosis—a siege of schizophrenialike symptoms that appear suddenly, last a few days, and

There is evidence that babies of low birth weight have a higher risk of developing schizophrenia later in life, possibly because their treatment requires more frequent separation from their mother.

then disappear, usually without lasting ill effect. But there is no solid evidence that stress is the underlying factor that produces true schizophrenia. If stress causes the illness, why are not epidemics of schizophrenia common in high-stress situations? Indeed, as psychiatrist E. Fuller Torrey has pointed out, the incidence of schizophrenia actually dropped in some countries during World War II.

A Combination of Causes

As a better, though still uncertain, understanding of the biological aspects of schizophrenia has emerged, the psychological and social theories of the cause of schizophrenia have lost much of their once-powerful appeal. Years of research have failed to show that the cause of schizophrenia lies in the ego or the libido.

Furthermore, if parents or family interactions are solely to blame, why do only a small percentage of children who have a schizophrenic mother or father ever develop the disease? It is difficult to see how parents, family relationships, or stress could create the abnormalities in brain structure and function found in many schizophrenics. Still, old ideas die hard, and each of them continues to find some support as *the* cause of schizophrenia—more often among the general public than among mental-health professionals.

The studies of twins cited in Chapter 4 clearly showed that inherited genes play a role in schizophrenia. Adoption studies have shown that placing a child born to nonschizophrenic parents into a household where one of the adopting parents suffers the disease does not increase the child's risk of becoming schizophrenic. Does that mean we can dismiss psychological and social events as having no role in the disease? Absolutely not.

Those same studies of twins that revealed a genetic component of schizophrenia also demonstrated that more than inheritance is involved in the disease. That identical twins do not have a 100% concordance for schizophrenia strongly indicates that environmental factors must be important contributors to the devastating disease. It is well known that some genetic traits are influenced to one degree or another by the environment. Height, for example, depends to some degree on diet. A person's level of intelligence is partly determined by learning experiences and opportunities as well as diet. And new evidence emerging from an international study suggests that becoming schizophrenic may partly depend on specific family interactions, physical problems, and, perhaps, difficulties in social adjustment.

Risk Factors

Researchers from 15 major medical centers in the United States and abroad are cooperating in a long-term effort to identify the risk factors of schizophrenia. Risk factors increase a person's chances of developing some ailment. The most familiar are those that contribute to heart disease, particularly attacks—high blood pressure, high cholesterol levels in the blood, cigarette smoking, and a family history of heart attacks. Having a risk factor is no guarantee a person will suffer the disease; it does mean that the person's odds of developing an illness are greater than those of someone without risk factors. The more risk factors an individual has, the greater the chances the disease will occur.

The international High-Risk Consortium study is based on the assumption that people may inherit a predisposition to schizophrenia, but this predisposition alone does not mean that people will develop the disease. Only if they are affected by some environmental factors will schizophrenia occur. Thus, the theory goes, certain life events ultimately determine whether someone with a genetic vulnerability actually becomes ill. More than 3,000 young children have been enrolled in this study. The purpose of the study is to see which individuals actually suffer the disease and what events in their lives set them apart from those at high risk who do not. Based on their family histories, each child had a risk at least six times greater than other children of developing schizophrenia. Results so far must be considered preliminary, and researchers have not attempted to say which of the risk factors may be more likely than others to precipitate schizophrenia. But their findings are intriguing.

One risk factor is linked to family communications. Children in the study whose parents regularly give them confusing and negative messages appear more likely to develop schizophrenia. Typically, these parents engage in what one researcher has called "character assassination." They attack and denigrate the child, criticizing the person rather than his or her behavior, statements, or ideas. The child may hear over and over: "You're no good," "You're stupid," or "Can't you ever do anything right?" Later, the parents tell the child the statements really are not true. Such conflicting messages delivered by the parents can create great confusion in the child. Such parents often tell their child what he or she is thinking and feeling. Statements such as "You really don't like soccer" or "You hate your new teacher" leave the child confused about what his own thoughts really are. It is a sad truth that "crazier" parents will talk in crazier ways to their children, who are thereby further endangered. Researchers do not believe confusing communications would lead to schizophrenia in someone who was not genetically susceptible, although they do cause other psychological harm. In a person with a genetic predisposition for schizophrenia, however, an endless stream of such comments might so confuse and disrupt the child's thought processes that a break with reality could result.

Children in the study seemed more likely to develop schizophrenia if they were separated from their parents and passed from one relative to another or were raised in institutions or by foster parents. The disease also was more likely to occur in people whose mothers had poor emotional bonding with them in early infancy. Among children with schizophrenic mothers, the child's risk of schizophrenia was greater if the mother's disease was severe, if its onset was earlier, or if its duration was longer. Poor coordination in early life or complications at birth, such as a low birth weight or abnormal position in the womb prior to delivery, also appeared to increase a child's risk.

A group of problems that tended to be noticed most in school also appeared to increase risk. These included a short attention span, poor short-term memory, inadequate verbal skills, a high level of anger, and abrasive, disruptive, and aggressive behavior. What remains a question is whether these are true risk factors or whether they are early warning signs that schizophrenia is just developing and the full-blown symptoms are still a few years away.

Though schizophrenia does not usually set in until early adolescence, preschizophrenic behavior may manifest itself earlier, in the form of unusual aggressiveness or inattentiveness.

Research has shown how complex a disease schizophrenia is. The realization that the illness almost certainly involves both genetics and life events has greatly advanced science's understanding of the disorder. Sorting out precisely what environmental factors can tip a vulnerable person from sanity to madness may one day tell doctors how they can prevent at least some cases of schizophrenia.

•   •   •   •

CHAPTER 6

. . . .

ANTIPSYCHOTIC DRUGS

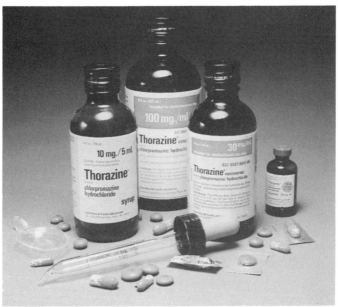

Thorazine, trade name of chlorpromazine

In the early 1950s, quite by accident, there emerged an anti-psychotic that revolutionized the treatment of schizophrenia. The drug was chlorpromazine, and the company that developed it never envisioned it as a medication for the mentally ill. It was meant to be an antihistamine, one of a large group of drugs used primarily to treat allergies, but in animal tests it only made the animals tired. So the new drug sat on a shelf for years.

Dr. Henri Laborit, a French surgeon, wanted a drug that would calm surgery patients about to receive anesthesia. He decided that a strong sedating antihistamine might be just what was needed. The drug he tried was chlorpromazine. He found that it not only calmed patients but also detached them from their environment without actually putting them to sleep. So impressed was Laborit that he recommended the drug to several psychiatrists. Dr. Jean Delay and Dr. Pierre Deniker were even more amazed by their results when they gave chlorpromazine to hospitalized schizophrenics. It not only calmed hyperactive patients but also brought other patients out of their withdrawal and seemed to reduce some of the major symptoms of the disease.

No drug had ever been found that reduced the symptoms of schizophrenia. Barbiturates were commonly given to pacify schizophrenics, but no one pretended that they actually affected the disease itself. Reports of chlorpromazine's remarkable success quickly spread its use throughout Europe. By 1956, it was widely prescribed in the United States under the trade name Thorazine. Scientific tests have proved over and over that chlorpromazine and the nearly two dozen antischizophrenic medications that followed it can profoundly alter the disease's symptoms and improve the lives of those with the misfortune to suffer it.

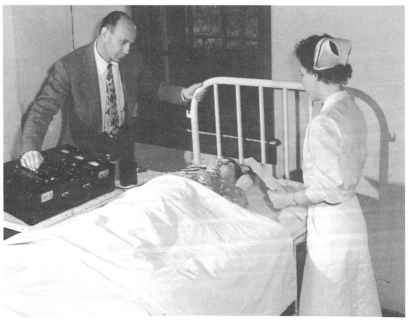

For many years, electroconvulsive therapy (ECT) was commonly used to curb schizophrenics' aggressiveness. Now it is generally used only in cases of severe depression.

This 17th-century painting by Hieronymous Bosch makes sport of the belief that the insane could be cured with surgery. The frontal lobotomy, the effectiveness of which has proven to be minimal, was a common operation until the 1970s.

The drugs used to treat schizophrenics are generally called antipsychotics. They are also referred to as neuroleptics or major tranquilizers, although some have no tranquilizing effect whatsoever. Before the discovery of antipsychotic drugs, the treatment of schizophrenia had been spectacularly unsuccessful. The much-heralded psychoanalytic techniques of Sigmund Freud proved useless in repairing the schizophrenic's break with reality. However, the consequences of this failure were mild compared to those of some physical "treatments"—the chainings and whippings of the mentally ill that occurred in earlier times, for example.

Three False Starts

This century has seen some well-intended therapies carried out with little scientific basis and with unhappy results. These include the insulin coma, electroconvulsive therapy, and a form of surgery called the frontal lobotomy.

Insulin is a hormone in the body that helps control the level of sugar in the blood. It is used to treat diabetics who cannot make insulin on their own. If too much insulin is given, the supply

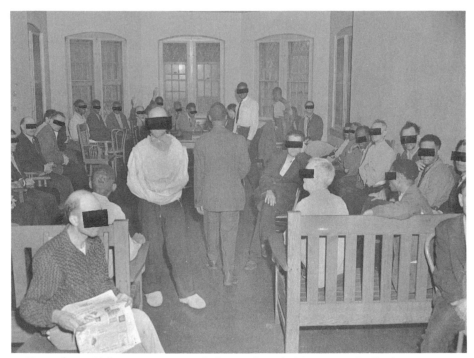

The enforced idleness at a crowded state hospital has a tragically deteriorating effect on those who might otherwise recover. Therapeutic drugs have allowed many to be released.

of sugar to the brain is reduced to the point where coma occurs. And this can cause death. A German physician named Manfred Sakel induced insulin coma in some morphine addicts to relieve their severe withdrawal symptoms. He also tried the technique on other disorders and concluded in 1933 that it helped schizophrenics. Doctors in Europe and the United States rushed to induce insulin coma in severe schizophrenics. Some patients died as a result, without any evidence that excessive insulin truly ameliorated symptoms of the disease.

Electroconvulsive therapy (ECT) is another example of a therapy once widely used with little evidence of its usefulness. In ECT, brief pulses of electricity are passed through the brain. ECT has proved very effective in helping some people with severe depression, but the evidence from its use in thousands of schizophrenics is that it has little or no effect on their illness.

Perhaps the most outrageous "therapy" for schizophrenia in this century is the frontal lobotomy. The American psychiatrist

Solomon H. Snyder has called it "barbaric" and "diabolical." A frontal lobotomy is the surgical removal of parts of the front of the brain. The operation was developed in 1935 by Dr. Egas Moniz of Portugal. He believed the site of the schizophrenic's mental problems lay in the brain's frontal lobes. He reached this conclusion in part because of animal experiments that showed that the operation made monkeys and cats very docile. In humans, the surgery did produce a quieter patient, and it was used on tens of thousands of schizophrenics in Europe and the United States. There is no evidence, however, that frontal lobotomy provided any improvement in the disease—or did any more than rob schizophrenics of what shreds of personality they had left.

Progress Is Made . . .

Chlorpromazine revolutionized the treatment of schizophrenia. Forty years ago, a diagnosis of schizophrenia meant many years— perhaps decades or a lifetime—in an institution. Mental hospitals were crowded with "hopeless" cases, and their numbers kept increasing. In 1955, there were 560,000 hospitalized mental pa-

An unfortunate consequence of drug therapy is that too many schizophrenics and other mentally ill persons have been sent out on their own. Thousands have ended up on the streets, swelling the ranks of the homeless.

tients in the United States, up from 462,000 in 1946. At least half were schizophrenics. The use of antipsychotic drugs helped reverse this trend. In the 15 years after chlorpromazine first found widespread use in the United States, the number of patients in mental hospitals dropped 50%. The antipsychotics were not the only factor, but they were a major one. These drugs dramatically altered the often hopeless outlook that once confronted schizophrenics by reducing symptoms, sharply cutting the time most schizophrenics had to spend in hospitals, and lessening their chances of being rehospitalized. Without these medications, it would be impossible to treat chronic schizophrenics at home.

. . . And Problems, Too

Unfortunately, the emptying of the schizophrenia wards has produced its own problems. In 1963, the U.S. Congress passed an act that inadvertently worsened the schizophrenics' situation. The idea was that the mentally ill—those with schizophrenia, severe personality disorders, brain damage, and other disabling conditions—would be better off living in their local communities. The states and local governments were to provide programs and outpatient treatment facilities for the mentally ill. The idea never fulfilled its expectations. There was never enough money spent to provide the needed care. As a result, many of the chronically mentally ill, including a large number of schizophrenics, joined the ranks of the homeless. Many went to big cities instead of back home. They were reduced to prowling and begging on streets, sometimes sleeping in the open, sometimes in shelters run by cities or charitable groups. Without supervision and encouragement to take their antipsychotic drugs, these schizophrenics have no hope of controlling their disease. They live a disconnected existence devoid of reality. Many fall victim to violent crime, infections and other physical illnesses, malnutrition, and untimely death. Even the return of a schizophrenic to his or her home can create stresses that require psychological and social support for the family.

It is important to remember that antipsychiotic drugs do not cure schizophrenia. What they can do is control many of its debilitating symptoms and allow schizophrenics to live a more normal life. Antipsychotics are more akin to the use of insulin in diabetes or the medications used to control epilepsy. If patients stop taking their drugs, it is highly likely their symptoms will return.

with family	8000,000
alone	200,000
nursing homes	300,000
foster, group homes	300,000
hospitals	200,000
public shelters, streets	150,000
jail	26,000

Though it is normally best for the schizophrenic patient to live with his or her family, some need more professional care. Others, as this chart shows, have the benefit of neither.

Antipsychotics are not equally effective against all of schizophrenia's symptoms. They work principally against delusions, hallucinations, aggressive actions, and bizarre behavior and thoughts. The drugs are much less effective against the flat emotions, apathy, and withdrawal symptoms that characterize schizophrenia and the less specific problems of agitation and anxiety that frequently accompany the disease. Nor do antipsychotics always eliminate the symptoms they work best against. Patients may continue to experience occasional delusions, hallucinations, and other symptoms even when they take their medications unfailingly. It is estimated, for example, that the drugs are 80 to 90% effective in totally stopping the "voices" that many schizophrenics hear.

The Drugs' Many Effects

Chlorpromazine was followed by the development of other antipsychotic drugs. Their chemical compositions and their mechanisms of action vary somewhat, but they share a common end result: They all block the action of dopamine in the brain. No one, however, knows why interfering with dopamine relieves the symptoms of schizophrenia.

The antipsychotics are not equally effective in all people. This variance is not uncommon among drugs. Each hay-fever sufferer, for example, reacts a bit differently to each antihistamine. Sim-

Paul Robeson in the 1933 film The Emperor Jones. *Hearing voices is a common delusion among schizophrenics, but it can be treated with chlorpromazine.*

ilarly, physicians cannot always determine which antipsychotic will be best for a particular schizophrenic. Generally, if a person has improved on an antipsychotic before or if someone in the patient's family has been helped by the drug, the drug is likely to work in that individual. But there are exceptions even to this broad rule.

If a schizophrenic fails to respond to a specific antipsychotic, a physician will try another. If the second drug gives no relief, a third will be tried, and so on through the catalog of available antipsychotics. Different people also respond differently to the same drug. So in trying an antipsychotic, a physician usually will increase the dosage before abandoning the drug and moving on to another.

Side Effects of the Drugs Antipsychotics are surprisingly safe drugs, given the powerful influence they exert on the brain. Physicians regard them as among the safer prescription drugs marketed. An overdose does not kill. They are not addictive. And they do not create tolerance—that is, people do not have to take larger and larger doses to get the same effect. However, as every physician knows, and every patient should, no drug is perfectly safe. All drugs cause some adverse reactions, and the antipsychotics are no exception. Sometimes their side effects are so severe that the patient is forced to discontinue their use. The incidence of such side effects varies from drug to drug, as do the reactions of people to them. Fortunately, however, another antipsychotic often can be found to replace the one causing problems.

Common side effects of antipsychotic drugs include constipation, drowsiness, a dry mouth, and blurred vision. Usually these diminish or disappear after a few weeks. Less likely to disappear on their own are such common side effects as restlessness, slurred speech, trembling of the hands and feet, and muscle rigidity in the head and neck. (This second group of problems can often be handled by giving a second drug, one from a group known as the anticholinergics.) Potentially the most serious common side effects of the antipsychotics are a greatly increased sensitivity to sun that can result in severe sunburn; a tendency to faint when rising from a lying to a standing position; and weight gain of 100 pounds or more, which increases the risk of other diseases and early death.

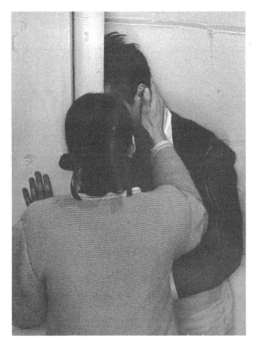

Antipsychotic drugs must be coupled with rehabilitation and human understanding if the patient is to return to society.

Among the less common and less serious adverse drug reactions seen in schizophrenics are rashes, heavy salivation, appetite loss, and—in women—menstrual-cycle disturbances and the discharge of fluids from the breasts. Occasionally, more serious side effects are seen, such as eye and liver damage, convulsions, urinary- and intestinal-tract blockages, and a decrease in the body's disease-fighting white blood cells. A decrease in sexual desire in both sexes and impotency in men sometimes occurs with the antipsychotics. But whether these problems are serious depends on the patient's view. If he or she had no interest in sex prior to taking the drugs, then the patient may regard any sexual side effects as inconsequential. If, however, the patient pursued an active sex life, a diminished drive is a matter of serious concern to him.

Probably the most feared side effect of the antipsychotic drugs is a condition called tardive dyskinesia. Its most common symptoms are repetitive, involuntary movements of the tongue, mouth, and face. These include sucking and chewing motions, lip smacking, and thrusting the tongue into the cheek. Sometimes the arms and legs and even the trunk of the body are affected by jerking and twitching movements. Tardive dyskinesia occurs in about 10 to 15% of people who take antipsychotics, usually those over age 50 who have used the drugs for many years. The condition generally disappears once a person stops taking their antipsychotic. In some cases, it persists for unknown reasons. The problem with stopping a chronic schizophrenic's medication is that his psychotic symptoms return. To prevent this, many physicians try to strike a balance. They lower the person's dosage to a level that controls the symptoms of schizophrenia and at the same time minimizes the symptoms of tardive dyskinesia.

There are those who consider the antipsychotics true "wonder drugs" that have greatly improved the outlook for schizophrenics as compared to that period in history when there was no effective treatment for the disease. However, these drugs alone do little to help rehabilitate the schizophrenic and assist him in reentering society and the work force. Rehabilitation requires social, psychological, and vocational support and counseling as well as antipsychotic medications.

•   •   •   •

CHAPTER 7

. . . .

SUPPORTIVE THERAPIES

A person does not emerge instantaneously from an acute episode of schizophrenia. Reestablishing contact with reality or semblances of it takes time. The recovering schizophrenic is a vulnerable individual, racked by low self-esteem, disorganized, insecure, and confused by his personal life and future. Drugs can control many of schizophrenia's most noticeable symptoms—delusions and hallucinations, for example—but other symptoms are left little touched. Medications do nothing to relieve the problems of living, working, and readjusting to society. For this, the schizophrenic needs psychological, environmental, and skills counseling to assist him in reestablishing and maintaining his ties with reality and the working world. Mental-health experts increasingly stress a combination of drugs and determined, long-term counseling to help schizophrenics overcome their apathy and emotional difficulties.

Schizophrenics do have control over some of the factors that influence their recovery. Certainly a willingness to continue taking their antipsychotic drugs and to seek and remain in counseling is vital. The person assisting a schizophrenic's emotional and social problems may be the physican prescribing and monitoring the patient's medication, or it can be someone working in cooperation with the physician—a psychologist or psychiatric social worker, for example.

KINDS OF PSYCHOTHERAPY

The counseling given schizophrenics is often loosely referred to as psychotherapy, but it is important to realize that many quite different types of psychotherapy exist. The popular picture of a

The self-confidence and physical exertion needed for mountain climbing has helped some patients along the way to recovery.

patient lying on a couch and talking to a "headshrinker" does not apply to schizophrenia.

The common thread in all psychotherapies is that talking about oneself to a skilled therapist, who offers suggestions and advice, will help a person deal with psychological problems and adjust to life's trials and demands.

Perhaps the best-known psychotherapies are the group therapies that are known alternately as insight-oriented, expressive, or psychodynamic. Psychoanalysis, developed by Sigmund Freud and carried on by his followers, fits this category. The insight-oriented therapies seek to expose the conflicts of the subconscious mind and make the patient aware of them. Their focus is on exploring the patient's feelings, with great emphasis on events in the past. The therapist plays a passive role, providing only limited guidance as the patient struggles to understand how unconscious conflicts influence his feelings and how this affects his behavior.

For years psychoanalysts sought the cure for schizophrenia in the subconscious, but with little or no success. Other insight-oriented psychotherapies have proved no more useful. Studies show that schizophrenics who are treated with an insight-oriented psychotherapy do no better than those who are not. Moreover, there is some evidence that these psychotherapies may actually do harm. Several studies have indicated that insight-oriented treatment can make schizophrenics sicker. The reason may lie in the nature of the disease. The schizophrenic's mind is confused and disorganized. If such a person is asked to probe his subconscious for conflicts at the same time he is fighting to impose some order over his chaotic thoughts, the effort may be too overwhelming. As a result, the schizophrenic's own struggle for mental order is defeated, and his condition gets worse.

Supportive Therapy

Whereas insight-oriented psychotherapies have fallen into some disrepute in treating schizophrenia, the "supportive" psychotherapies have proved a useful adjunct to antipsychotic drugs. Several recent studies suggest the two combined are more effective than medications alone in reducing rehospitalization among schizophrenics. Although these supportive therapies also rely on talk, their focus and goals are quite different from those of insight-oriented psychotherapies. Supportive psychotherapies emphasize support and providing structure to the patient's life. They focus on the schizophrenic's behavior. The aim is to help patients distinguish fact from fantasy, to learn or relearn social skills, to cope with the world around them, and to make the most that they can of their lives. The supportive therapist is actively a friend, guide, adviser, sounding board, and teacher. For this to occur, the therapist and patient must form a strong, trusting relationship. This may take many months, for schizophrenia leaves people suspicious and distrusting, even of those who would help them.

The supportive therapist provides recovering schizophrenics with a means to test their thoughts and behavior against reality. Even with their antipsychotic medications, schizophrenics often cling to irrational ideas for many months. Delusions of being spied on or of possessing mystical powers, for example, may linger to confuse the schizophrenic. With a trusted therapist, the patient can discuss his or her thoughts and see which ones comport with reality. This kind of therapy, when accompanied by drug therapy, can help reduce or eliminate the disoriented thoughts that plague schizophrenics. In the same way, the patient can test whether his public behavior is proper. Do his conversations sound normal or are there still signs of disconnected thoughts? When he flared with anger, was he justified, and was his anger expressed in an appropriate way? The trained supportive therapist will listen, advise, and encourage the patient as he struggles to sort out his reentry into society.

The Therapist's Many Roles The schizophrenic's gradual break with reality, which often occurs in the late teens, frequently leaves him or her ill equipped to deal with people. The supportive therapist plays a key role in helping the schizophrenic learn or relearn social skills—how to behave when introduced to someone, how to make polite conversation, how to dress and act during a job interview. Something as seemingly simple as role playing and encouragement may help enormously. If a young man is frightened and unsure of how to ask for a date, the therapist will offer advice on how to make the approach. Then the therapist will play the part of the young woman, offering the young man encouragement and support to build his confidence. Finally, after the young man has asked for a date, the therapist will talk with him about it, evaluating his performance and offering useful suggestions for the future.

The onset of schizophrenia often occurs in the teen years, preventing the person from learning normal social skills. He or she is then in danger of becoming isolated.

Helping the schizophrenic deal with stress is equally important. Stress in schizophrenia is akin to stress in asthma: It does not cause the disease, but it can aggravate it. Together, the patient and therapist can determine which people, which situations, and which tasks generate emotional stress in the patient. Then the therapist can guide the patient in learning to handle stress. In some situations, handling it may mean avoiding the stress-provoking individual or circumstance. In others, mental techniques to counter and reduce stress can be learned.

An important part of the therapist's job is to educate his patients about their illness. Schizophrenics should understand the nature of their disease and how it will affect them in the future. That genetics plays some role in schizophrenia may affect their decision to have children. The disease's often episodic nature and the failure of antipsychotic drugs to control all symptoms means that a schizophrenic is unlikely ever to live a totally normal life. The therapist can explore the difficulties that lie ahead, explaining that factors outside the schizophrenic's control can limit his achievement. It is important for schizophrenics to realize that it is these factors—and not their lack of willpower, brain power, or inner drive—that prevent them from accomplishing all they might hope to achieve. The therapist must help schizophrenics understand and accept the obstacles their illness presents without discouraging them from trying to achieve all they can.

Relapses frequently do occur in schizophrenia. The therapist must discuss this possibility with his patients. Some patients sense, when experiencing problems such as a specific sleep disorder or increased agitation, that they are about to suffer another severe break with reality. There is evidence to suggest that certain other signs are often apparent about a week before an acute relapse occurs. These include depression, paranoia, and personal conflict. Alerting patients, their family, and friends to these "pre-schizophrenic" symptoms may help lessen the impact of a relapse. If an oncoming attack is suspected, antipsychotic drugs can be started again or their dosage increased.

A member of the Fountain House clubhouse (left) and a staff worker use a video camera to film the in-house TV program. The staff and members work together in all aspects of running the facility.

Group Therapy

Supportive group psychotherapy also can help the recovering schizophrenic. This is particularly true of groups that focus on schizophrenia education and the development of social skills. Generally, such groups consist of 4 to 8 patients, usually no more than 10, and 1 or 2 therapists. The emphasis of such groups is on the problems their members encounter in the real world and how to deal with them. As in individual therapy, the patient can test his ideas and behavior against reality. Here the feedback comes not just from a therapist but from others who are recovering from the same illness. Therapists guide group discussions so that members get positive and useful comments without fear of personal attack or criticism. Again, role playing can be extremely helpful not only to the persons acting out social situations but to those watching. A particularly shy or frightened member of the group may learn social skills and gain confidence as he observes and listens to others working through their own problems.

A great benefit of group therapy is the realization by its members, the gut understanding, that they are not alone in their suffering. People may read extensively about their mental illness and how the disease affects its victims. Yet inside they feel as if no one can truly understand the emotional horrors or embarrassments they have suffered. Thus, there is enormous relief in talking with others who have shared the same or similar experiences. This can help ease the guilt, tension, anger, and isolation so many recovering schizophrenics feel.

Other Therapies

It should be remembered that the use of different kinds of group therapy will always depend on the patient's needs and abilities. One kind of group will work for a person who lives with his or her family, but in most cases a person who lives alone needs a different kind of treatment. Network therapy is an approach that has been tried with some success in a few cities to aid schizophrenics—mostly people who have lost contact with relatives and old friends and are increasingly isolated and alone—who live away from their families. The process begins when a therapist calls together all the people who know the schizophrenic and who might help him. Each is asked to offer a little emotional support and encouragement to the schizophrenic. Help may take the form of telephone calls, occasional invitations to dinner, or driving the individual to church each week.

One type of treatment that has gained credibility in the last few years is creative art therapy. For the patient unable to address his or her illness in the usual verbal manner, the mere act of painting, dancing, writing, or singing can prove beneficial. Patients are encouraged to express themselves through body movements or by writing poetry, for instance. The patient teaches him- or herself some boundaries in this way and can develop a more organized rhythm and use it for creative expression. In one recent case, an elderly woman with a life history of mental illness managed to cure herself over the course of a few years by drawing self-portraits without looking in a mirror; gradually her self-image became healthier, more in tune with reality. Her sketches are viewed by some, in fact, as being quite good. Though creative art therapies cannot be the primary treatment for all schizophrenics, the nonverbal and nontraditional approach does allow some of them an important release.

The clubhouse model was first tried for the mentally ill, including schizophrenics, in 1948, by an organization in New York called Fountain House. There are now 180 such facilities in the United States and a few overseas, and the approach is gaining greater acceptance in psychiatric circles. In a clubhouse, the mentally ill are members rather than patients or clients. They are given a wide range of opportunities to use their time constructively, working alongside staff at running the clubhouse. As they discover their capabilities, they may apply their new skills to paid part-time jobs through a transitional employment program; today 135 people per day go to work from Fountain House, for 40 New York City firms. Eventually, if they are able, some patients will call on the clubhouse's ongoing support program to assist them in finding full-time work. Even the most disabled persons are given the chance to succeed or fail on their own terms, including the chance to have their own apartment if they can manage it. Advocates of the clubhouse approach to the treatment of schizophrenia maintain that recovery rates have been encouragingly high.

In recent years, a technique called "family management" has become an important part of the treatment of recovering schizophrenics. University of Pittsburgh researchers have found that

this approach significantly improves the recovery of a schizophrenic who returns home after hospitalization. Family management gives emotional support and education about the disease.
It seeks to promote a calmer climate within the household. Families are told what is known about the role of genetic and environmental factors in schizophrenia. Therapists try to ease their
guilt and sense of blame that they are somehow responsible for
the illness. Family members are taught how better to care for
their schizophrenic child until he or she can live outside the
home. Great emphasis is placed on keeping stress as low as possible. Families learn ways to deal with the schizophrenic member's peculiar behavior and demands. The recovering schizophrenic
may be suspicious, aggressive, and still troubled by some delusions, hallucinations, and bizarre thinking. As psychologist Daniel Goleman has pointed out, it can be quite trying for any family
to live with someone who insists the television set must be wrapped
in aluminum foil to prevent eavesdropping. Family management
teaches the need to avoid the extremes of intense conflict and
severe criticism on the one hand and a blind optimism and Pol-
lyanna enthusiasm on the other. And family members are also

*Supportive therapy can give the patient the caring and assistance he or she needs
to ease back into society.*

urged to set reasonable rules for the schizophrenic, for both the patient's well-being and their own.

Supportive therapies have proved to be of considerable benefit to both schizophrenics and their families, but such programs are expensive. They require the time and effort of one or more highly trained individuals. Many schizophrenics or their families cannot afford the cost of private support therapies. Even those whose health plans cover psychiatric care often find their insurance inadequate. Government and charitable mental-health programs are woefully short of funds to meet the nation's needs. The result is that in America, as elsewhere, there are thousands of schizophrenics who are living out lives in a netherworld between madness and sanity, even though they are surrounded by people who love and care about them. It is in this loving embrace that schizophrenia produces some of its most tragic repercussions.

•   •   •   •

CHAPTER 8

. . . .

THE FAMILY

Families are the forgotten victims of schizophrenia. It is not simply the schizophrenic who suffers from his or her illness. A serious, chronic mental disease affects the entire family—psychologically, emotionally, and financially. There is first the shock of the victim's acute break with reality, then the years of anguish that follow as patient and family struggle with the effects of the illness and the efforts at recovery. Family members, to one degree or another, will suffer worry, guilt, fear, embarrassment, blame, and stress.

Here are just a few comments from people who have schizophrenics in their families. They are drawn from Maryellen Walsh's *Schizophrenia: Straight Talk for Family and Friends*:

"We feel like we have lost a child."

"I don't know how my other children feel about it. We can't talk without crying."

"My son told me he thought of killing himself and also me because he knew I would find his death so painful."

"My relationship with my husband became cold. I seemed dead inside and couldn't respond to his attentions."

"It tears a family apart. Each has his own idea as to how schizophrenia should be handled, which causes severe friction, even between husband and wife."

"He entered a track meet stark naked."

"I tell myself not to worry, even professionals can't handle this disease. I feel guilty anyhow."

"Was it something we did to him?"

"We don't know what it was, what to do, where to go, how to act, what to think."

"This has been by far our biggest problem: accepting the fact that he is chronically ill, that he will be that way his whole life, and that we must deal with it for the rest of ours."

"It haunts us every day—what will happen to him after we're gone."

Returning to the Family

About two-thirds of hospitalized schizophrenics return to live with family members, usually parents. Many others live near their families. Most continue to show symptoms even when taking their antipsychotic medications. Although the worst signs of their illness may be controlled, they may suffer residual delusions and hallucinations, exhibit odd behavior, retreat socially and emotionally, neglect their appearance, and become moody, sullen, apathetic, and even hostile. It is not easy living with someone who twists almost everything you say into a sinister threat, who suddenly bursts out laughing for no reason, or who talks back to voices that exist only in his hallucinating mind. Moreover, dealing with a loved one who closets himself in a bedroom and accuses the family of trying to poison him can try the patience and stamina of the most loving parent, sibling, or spouse.

Relatives of a schizo-phrenic may feel embar-rassment or may blame the ill person for all of their problems. In many cases, the whole family may need help in coping with the illness.

Social withdrawal and the inability to interact and form normal relationships with other humans are the most obvious problems for most returning schizophrenics. As the days, weeks, and months go by, the inability to reach the "old" healthy child, sibling, or spouse becomes increasingly distressful for family members. They remember "back when," before the disease transformed the mind of their loved one, and wonder why the schizophrenic is not returning to normal. The rejection hurts, and although the family may realize this rejection is part of the disease and not a personal slap at them, they still may become resentful and hostile themselves.

Many families see getting the schizophrenic back to work as a sure sign of recovery. But the withdrawal problems may hamper or prevent the patient from resuming or starting a job. The patient may not want to go back to earning a living. Schizophrenics do not lose their intelligence. Many realize their illness has robbed them of the skills and concentration required by the careers they trained for or expected. Some will accept more menial jobs, working with people who have neither their intelligence nor their interests. Others resist and prefer remaining at home, perhaps to stay in bed most of the day. The inability of the schizophrenic to return to work, for whatever reason, can emotionally affect both the patient and his family.

Fears Within the Family Families frequently fear that the schizophrenic will become aggressive or violent. Indeed, schizophrenics can be hostile and aggressive. Episodes of aggressive behavior are usually short lived and result because the person feels under great pressure for some reason or panics because he senses some threat. Truly violent behavior is uncommon. When a schizophrenic commits a violent act, it is usually because he is suffering a paranoid delusion that someone is trying to harm him or because his hallucinations order him to attack.

Another common fear among families is that the schizophrenic will kill himself. Suicide is not a common problem in schizophrenia. Nonetheless, there is an increased risk that a person

The schizophrenic may at times seem completely cut off from the family's emotional life, as depicted in this 19th-century engraving.

Bizarre behavior is an occasional characteristic of schizophrenia. This woman was undressing in public when the police intervened.

suffering the disorder will take his own life. The threat is greatest during an acute attack, when the person's break with reality is greatest. Frequently, such suicides result from grandiose delusions or in response to voices that demand the person's self-destruction. Some schizophrenics suffer delusions that they are immortal or indestructible or that they can fly or walk on water.

It is not unusual for people who suffer schizophrenia to become depressed as a result of their illness. Depression as a reaction to schizophrenia is easily understood. The recovering schizophrenic has suffered through an enormously debilitating experience. As he contemplates his future—uncertain whether he will experience another acute break with reality and unsure of how well he will recover—the schizophrenic may see his problems as so overwhelmingly insurmountable that he suffers a bout of depression. He sinks into feelings of hopelessness and worth-

Vincent Van Gogh, whose form of mental illness was not diagnosed, cut off his ear and, at age 37, committed suicide. Families often fear violent behavior on the part of a schizophrenic relative, but in fact such outbursts are uncommon.

lessness. He may become listless, apathetic, and withdrawn—symptoms the family and even a physician might mistake as schizophrenic. Thus, family and patient may live through a troubled period that might be eliminated or reduced if the true cause of the symptoms was recognized and treated.

The Danger of Assigning Blame

Guilt and blame haunt the families of schizophrenics, making acceptance of the illness and living with the ill person even more difficult. Parents and spouses alike tend to blame themselves for their loved one's illness. "Was it something we did wrong in raising him?" "What did I do? She was never sick until I married her." "If only I had gotten him psychiatric help earlier." Even the schizophrenic's younger siblings may blame themselves. Youngsters may feel responsible because they had not been obedient enough, because they were jealous of the older brother or sister, or because in a fit of anger they had said they wished the ill sibling were dead. Such feelings of guilt are normal. Victims of robbery, rape, or assault frequently feel they are somehow to blame for what happened to them, but even when people recognize that their feelings of guilt are an unjustified reaction, it is still difficult to overcome a sense of self-blame.

Dismayed at the schizophrenic's state of mind and stricken by their own sense of guilt, parents, spouses, or siblings may begin blaming other family members. "If her father had paid any attention to her, this would never have happened." "His mother raised him as a wimp." "His father's side of the family was always crazy." Relatives, from grandparents to cousins, are equally likely to attribute the illness to someone within the family, usually the mother or father. Friends and neighbors and even some physicians will readily blame the parents in spite of what is now known about the interaction of genetic inheritance and environmental factors. The concept of the schizophrenia-causing parent is still alive, though not well founded. Torn by their own guilt and blamed by others, family members may suffer enormous emotional ups and downs as they struggle to cope with the schizophrenic and his odd actions and demands.

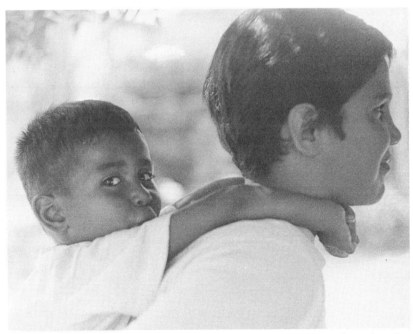

Siblings especially can feel the guilt and fear of having a schizophrenic in the family.

From Blame to Embarrassment

Along with guilt and blame, families suffer embarrassment from having a schizophrenic relative. Although science has learned that mental illnesses are true illnesses and not willful misbehavior or the work of evil spirits, there is still an enormous stigma attached to them. People who suffer a psychiatric disorder or who have "a crazy" or "a nut" in their family are looked down on in many societies. When a mental illness strikes, family members anticipate the reactions of others. They often will be embarrassed by the schizophrenic's behavior because they fear what friends and relatives will think or how they may respond. Even relatives who are not members of the immediate family may feel embarrassed by the presence of the schizophrenic and how others may perceive them.

Most adults will try to be polite and ignore the behavior of a friend's schizophrenic child or spouse unless it is particularly bizarre. Nonetheless, the family often senses an uneasiness and uncomfortableness, if not an outright disapproval or rejection. Children, particularly when away from adults, are likely to be less kind and more outspoken. They can be quite ruthless and nasty in their remarks about another child's schizophrenic sibling or parent. As a result, adults and children in a family with a schizophrenic member may gradually withdraw from friends and even other relatives. Some spend years in self-imposed social isolation, lonely and resentful about what fate has left them.

Sorting Out the Future

Families share the schizophrenic's concerns about the future. They are troubled about the prospects for the schizophrenic's recovery and the possibility of relapses.

They also have separate worries about the ill family member. Parents eventually wonder what will happen to the chronic schizophrenic after they die or become too old to provide care. Sisters and brothers may worry whether they will have to assume the care or at least the financial burden of the schizophrenic. Younger siblings commonly live with the fear that they, too, will become schizophrenic. This is particularly true if their parents seem concerned themselves about the possibility and seem to be trying to assess whether every unusual act or childish outburst is an early

Family members of schizophrenics have become organized in recent decades. Some of their activities include providing support for one another and leading the way toward better education and treatment programs for the ill.

sign of the disease. As they grow older, siblings may become fearful that their own children will inherit the family's malignant genes and develop schizophrenia. Such psychological burdens can exact an enormous toll on a family, one the schizophrenic is unaware of or unconcerned about.

Thus, schizophrenia can be a devastating illness, not just for those who suffer from it but to their families, as well. One man detailed the monetary costs in the first nine years after his son was diagnosed with schizophrenia. The boy had been hospitalized 10 times in that period for a total of 68 months. His medical expenses totaled $721,000. Health insurance covered $541,000 of this, but the family had to pay the remaining $180,000. Most families do not and cannot pay such huge medical bills, but stories of spending tens of thousands of dollars to help a schizophrenic son or daughter are common. Oftentimes, one member of the family, almost inevitably the mother, may give up working outside the house to care for the schizophrenic. This reduces the family's income and increases the drain on its financial resources.

Families and their individual members cope differently, and not always well, with the stresses of having a schizophrenic in their midst. Within any family it is rare for total agreement to exist as to how to deal with the ill member. As a result, conflicts within the family are inevitable, even frequent. Some members may be patient and unfailingly understanding of the schizophrenic's delusions, demands, and odd behavior. Others may find their tolerance tried and eventually exhausted. Still others may turn sarcastic and critical, barely suppressing or openly expressing their anger and hostility. In the end, some families adjust fairly well. Others may find the situation unbearable, to the point of driving the schizophrenic out of the home.

For some people, the stress of a schizophrenic living in the family can lead to discord, psychosomatic illness, depression, divorce, and even suicide. The formation of family support groups has helped many to cope with their problems, both with the schizophrenic and within themselves. Such groups offer family members a chance to talk out their problems, to learn about available social services and how others have handled similar situations, and to draw strength from other people who are coping with the same burdens.

•   •   •   •

CHAPTER 9

. . . .

PROGNOSIS

Is schizophrenia forever? Or do some people recover after many years of struggling with the illness? It is an important question—for patients, families, friends, physicians, and our entire social system. And the answer appears to be that schizophrenia does change over decades, that it is not always an unrelenting illness whose victims have no hope of getting better. Long-term studies in recent years indicate that a number of schizophrenics do recover or show significant improvement in their battle against the disease's debilitating symptoms.

New research suggests that people who have been institutionalized even for long periods may improve and become able to live on their own.

There is no question that some schizophrenics go downhill between diagnosis and death. Every psychiatrist who treats schizophrenics can cite cases in which the patient's illness became progressively worse, no matter what attempts at treatment were made. From its earliest days as a distinct form of mental illness, schizophrenia was considered an incurable ailment whose prognosis was inevitably bad. The apparently unremitting deterioration of patients with paranoid psychosis, hebephrenia, and catatonia was a key feature that led Emil Kraepelin in 1896, as we noted, to unite the three disorders into what he called dementia praecox and what we now call schizophrenia. Indeed, Kraepelin believed that anyone who improved after being diagnosed as suffering dementia praecox must have been misdiagnosed in the first place. Eugen Bleuler expanded Kraepelin's description of the disease, but he, too, came to view it as one from which there was no real recovery. Schizophrenia was thought so incurable that anyone who recovered from it was rediagnosed, after recovery, as having been only manic-depressive.

Many physicians did recognize that there were variations in the degree to which schizophrenia affected people. Both in Europe and the United States, some schizophrenics were considered to have a good prognosis and others a poor one. A good prognosis, however, usually meant the illness would be episodic—with alternating periods of remission and relapse—rather than unremitting. A person whose schizophrenia came on suddenly, was associated with some stressful event, and whose behavior was normal prior to his illness was generally considered to have a good prognosis. Someone whose break with reality came on slowly and for no apparent reason and who acted "odd" much of his life prior to becoming mentally ill was regarded as having a poor outlook. Generally, when schizophrenics were looked at 5 or 10 years after diagnosis, researchers found little sign of improvement in their illness. Such studies seemed to confirm the adage "Once a schizophrenic, always a schizophrenic."

The Recent Evidence: Five Studies

Since 1972, five long-term studies of schizophrenics have been published in Europe and the United States with some remarkable and quite similar findings. The schizophrenics in these studies

One schizophrenic's view of life resulted in this grotesque depiction. The man recovered and is now married.

were checked years after their diagnosis—the shortest average time between illness and final follow-up was 22 years, and the longest was 37 years. Each of the studies found that more than half the patients had recovered from their schizophrenia or had made significant improvement. However, the studies also confirmed that the future of some schizophrenics, is, indeed, one of endless illness and despair.

The first of these studies, which are changing psychiatry's view of schizophrenia's natural course and outcome, was carried out by Manfred Bleuler, the son of Eugen Bleuler and himself a distinguished psychiatrist. Manfred Bleuler followed 208 schizophrenics admitted to a hospital in Zurich, Switzerland, in 1942 and 1943. Some had been admitted for the first time; others had suffered relapses of their illness. Bleuler found that 20% of these 208 patients, after an average of 23 years, had recovered from their illness and that another 33% had shown significant improvement in the 5 years before the study ended. To Bleuler, a full recovery meant a former patient "could be fully employed in gainful work and that he could resume his former role in society." The group of schizophrenics who were admitted for the first time in 1942 and 1943 did even better. Twenty-three percent of them had fully recovered, and an additional 43% had shown significant improvement.

Another Swiss study of even longer duration also found eventual recovery among some schizophrenics. Researchers in Lausanne studied the mental health of 289 people an average of 37 years after they were first diagnosed as being schizophrenic. They found that 29% had recovered and that another 24% had significantly improved. And a West German research team found that among 502 schizophrenics, 26% had fully recovered in both psychological and social functioning an average of 22 years after their initial diagnosis. Another 31% showed significant improvement.

In the United States, two long-term studies have confirmed the European findings. Researchers in one study sought out 186 schizophrenics who had been admitted to the University Psychiatric Hospital in Iowa City, Iowa, between 1934 and 1944. The former mental patients were interviewed an average of 35 years after their admission. To the researchers' surprise, they found that 20% had recovered from their schizophrenic symptoms. Another 26% were considered significantly improved.

Doing useful work in the hospital generally gives the patient a better self-image. Partial or full recovery is possible for many patients.

Finally, the most recent study involved a group of 118 severely ill schizophrenics confined at the Vermont State Hospital in Waterbury during the mid-1950s. They had been mentally ill for an average of 16 years, and each had been hospitalized continuously for at least 6 years. They were poorly educated, socially withdrawn, exhibited inappropriate emotions, and suffered from delusions and hallucinations. Their chances of ever again leading productive lives were considered extremely low, if not zero.

Nonetheless, these patients took part in a pioneering job and psychological rehabilitation program. With aid and support from the communities in which they settled, they were released to live outside the hospital. Thirty-two years later, researchers interviewed those still living or the families of those who had died. They found that recovery or signficant improvement had occurred in well over half the patients. Among the 82 patients still alive, 34% were judged fully recovered, both psychologically and socially, and another 34% were significantly improved. Although most of these 82 former patients were in their sixties, 40% reported they had worked full time during the previous year.

Fountain House residents go to jobs outside of their facility. This woman is shown working at the Dow Jones Company in New York.

Some Cause for Optimism

Five long-term studies involving more than 1,300 patients have concluded—with striking consistency—that half or more of the schizophrenics had recovered or showed significant improvement in their illness after two to four decades. If, indeed, this is the case, then schizophrenia is a relentless, lifelong disease for less than half of its initial victims. It also suggests that environmental, psychological, and social factors may play a far more important role in a schizophrenic's progress than anyone realized. If so, learning what these factors are might lead to new ways to assist some schizophrenics along the path to recovery.

Results from the 5 studies have led Courtenay M. Harding of Yale University School of Medicine to suggest that recovery—when it occurs—may take 10 or even 20 years to start. Recently, she, Joseph Zubin of the University of Pittsburgh School of Medicine, and John S. Strauss, also of Yale, proposed that this long lag could have very unfortunate consequences. In their view, the time period is so long that by the time recovery might begin, families, physicians, and even patients themselves may have already given up hope and resigned themselves to a lifetime of illness.

Schizophrenia remains an incurable disease. Nonetheless, the drugs presently available help most schizophrenics most of the time. Less than 10% fail to respond, meaning that more than 90% of the victims of this devastating disease now benefit. One of the great disappointments to psychiatrists has been the failure to discover drugs more effective than today's antipsychotics. Nevertheless, research continues, and with the ongoing revolution in our understanding of the brain, new medications to treat schizophrenia are almost certain to be developed. Along with new drugs, new personal and social therapies and techniques are being developed to further improve the prognosis.

No one can predict which patients will suffer an unremitting illness, whose schizophrenia will be episodic, or who will eventually go on to recovery. Yet the findings that some schizophrenics do eventually and spontaneously recover have inspired new hopes. A diagnosis of schizophrenia remains serious and frightening, but at least the schizophrenic's outlook may not be as grim and dismal as was long believed.

•   •   •   •

FOR MORE INFORMATION

There are a number of national and local organizations that you can contact if you or someone you know would like further information or assistance regarding a psychological disorder or problem. The American Psychiatric Association (see below for address and phone number of the national office) can furnish printed materials on specific topics. It can also provide professional referrals in your area. In many places you can consult your local telephone directory for the branch of the American Psychiatric Association nearest your home. The following directory provides the addresses of major national mental health organizations. It also includes a state-by-state listing of associations affiliated with the National Alliance for the Mentally Ill, an advocacy group for the mentally ill.

UNITED STATES

National Organizations

American Academy of Child &
  Adolescent Psychiatry
3615 Wisconsin Avenue, N.W.
Washington, DC 20016
(202) 966-7300

American Association of Psychiatric
  Services for Children
1133 15th Street, N.W.
Suite 1000
Washington, DC 20005
(202) 429-9440

American Psychiatric Association
1400 K Street, N.W.
Washington, DC 20005
(202) 682-6000

National Alliance for the Mentally
  Ill
1901 North Fort Meyer Drive
Suite 500
Arlington, VA 22209
(703) 524-7600

National Association for Mental
  Health
1800 North Kent Street
Rosslyn, VA 22209

National Institute of Mental Health
5600 Fishers Lane, Room 15CO5
Rockville, MD 20857
(301) 443-4513

State Organizations

ALABAMA
Montgomery Alliance for the
  Mentally Ill
1743 Croom Drive
Montgomery, AL 36106

ALASKA
Alaska Alliance for the Mentally Ill
P.O. Box 2543
Fairbanks, AK 99707
(907) 457-3733

ARIZONA
Arizona Alliance for the Mentally Ill
11810 No. 45th Avenue
Glendale, AZ 85302
(602) 978-3952

ARKANSAS
Help and Hope, Inc.
Arkansas Families and Friends of
  the Mentally Ill
4313 W. Markham Hendrix Hall
  125
Little Rock, AR 72201
(501) 661-1548

CALIFORNIA
California Alliance for the Mentally
  Ill
2306 J St. #203
Sacramento, CA 95816
(916) 443-6417

COLORADO
Colorado Alliance for the Mentally
  Ill
P.O. Box 28008
Lakewood, CO 80228
(303) 321-3104

CONNECTICUT
Connecticut Alliance for the
  Mentally Ill
284 Battis Road
Hamden, CT 06514
(203) 248-3351

DELAWARE
New Castle Co. Alliance for the
  Mentally Ill
3705 Concord Pike
Wilmington, DE 19803
(302) 478-3060

DISTRICT OF COLUMBIA
Threshold-D.C.
2200 South Dakota Avenue, N.E.
Washington, DC 20018
(202) 636-4239

FLORIDA
Florida Alliance for the Mentally Ill
c/o Edward H. Gross
P.O. Box A-W
Port Salerno, FL 33492

GEORGIA
Georgia Alliance for the Mentally Ill
c/o Vicky Conn
1362 W. Peachtree Street
Atlanta, GA 30309
(404) 636-5735

HAWAII
Hawaii Families and Friends of
  Schizophrenics, Inc.
P.O. Box 10532
Honolulu, HI 96816
(808) 487-5456

IDAHO
Idaho Alliance for the Mentally Ill
321 Buchanan
American Falls, ID 83211
(208) 336-2346

ILLINOIS
Alliance for the Mentally Ill, Illinois
  State Coalition
P.O. Box 863
Glenview, IL 60025
(312) 729-1457

INDIANA

Indiana Alliance for the Mentally Ill
P.O. Box 8186
Ft. Wayne, IN 46808
(219) 432-4085

IOWA

Iowa Alliance for the Mentally Ill
509 E. 30th Street
Davenport, IA 52803
(319) 322-5845

KANSAS

Families for Mental Health
2708-A East Central
Wichita, KS 67214

KENTUCKY

Kentucky Alliance for the Mentally
Ill
c/o Kathleen Whipple
145 Constitution Avenue
Lexington, KY 40508
(606) 252-5518

LOUISIANA

Louisiana Alliance for the Mentally
Ill
1633 Letitia Street
Baton Rouge, LA 70808
(504) 344-2208

MAINE

Maine State Alliance for the
Mentally Ill, Inc.
P.O. Box 307
Oakland, ME 04963
(207) 547-3639

MARYLAND

Alliance for the Mentally Ill of
Maryland, Inc.
P.O. Box 336
Kensington, MD 20895
(301) 229-0928

MASSACHUSETTS

Alliance for the Mentally Ill of
Massachusetts, Inc.
34½ Beacon Street
Boston, MA 02108
(617) 367-8890

MICHIGAN

Alliance for the Mentally Ill of
Michigan
c/o Peggy Spitzig
17331 Fairfield
Livonia, MI 48152
(313) 421-4825

MINNESOTA

Alliance for the Mentally Ill of
Minnesota, Inc.
265 Ft. Rd. (W. 7th St.)
St. Paul, MN 55102
(612) 222-2741

MISSISSIPPI

Families and Friends of the
Mentally Ill
Rt. 9, Box 385
Hattiesburg, MS 39401
(601) 583-0948

MISSOURI

Missouri Alliance for the Mentally
Ill
135 W. Adams, Room G-9
St. Louis, MO 63122
(314) 966-4670

MONTANA

A New Beginning for the Mentally
Disordered
2405 39th Street
Missoula, MT 59807
(406) 251-2146

NEBRASKA

Western Nebraska Alliance for the
Mentally Ill
2280 Pacific Blvd.
Gering, NE 69341
(308) 436-7246

NEVADA

Nevada Alliance for the Mentally Ill
3970 Bryarcrest Court
Las Vegas, NV 89114
(702) 451-0755

NEW HAMPSHIRE

National Alliance for the Mentally
  Ill in New Hampshire
P.O. Box 544
Peterborough, NH 03458
(603) 924-3069

NEW JERSEY

New Jersey Alliance for the
  Mentally Ill
Box 101, Hoes Lane
Piscataway, NJ 08854
(201) 463-4059

NEW MEXICO

Alliance for the Mentally Ill, New
  Mexico
P.O. Box 876
Santa Fe, NM 87501
(505) 983-2584

NEW YORK

Alliance for the Mentally Ill of New
  York State
42 Elting Avenue
New Paltz, NY 12561
(914) 244-5134

Fountain House
425 W. 47th Street
New York, NY 10036
(212) 582-0340

NORTH CAROLINA

North Carolina Alliance for the
  Mentally Ill
P.O. Box 10557
Greensboro, NC 27404
(919) 275-7127

NORTH DAKOTA

REACH
505 19th St., S.W.
Minot, ND 58701
(701) 838-8905

OHIO

Ohio Alliance for the Mentally Ill
199 S. Central Ave.
Columbus, OH 43223
(614) 274-7000

OKLAHOMA

Concerned Citizens for Mental
  Health
5104 N. Francis, Suite B
Oklahoma City, OK 73118
(405) 524-6363

OREGON

Oregon Alliance for Advocates of
  the Mentally Ill
15693 S. Hidden Road
Mulino, OR 97042
(503) 632-3251

PENNSYLVANIA

Pennsylvania Alliance for the
  Mentally Ill
RD4, Box 942
Harrisburg, PA 17112
(717) 599-5998

RHODE ISLAND

East Bay Advocates
P.O. Box 168
Warren, RI 02885
(401) 245-2386

SOUTH CAROLINA

Greater Charleston Alliance for the
  Mentally Ill
P.O. Box 32084
Charleston, SC 29407-2538
(803) 795-4600

SOUTH DAKOTA

Northeastern MHC Family Support
  Group
Box 550
Aberdeen, SD 57401
(605) 225-1010

TENNESSEE

Tennessee Alliance for the Mentally
  Ill
416 E. Thompson Lane
Nashville, TN 37211
(615) 361-7950 or 7858

TEXAS
Texas Alliance for the Mentally Ill
P.O. Box 50434
Austin, TX 78759
(512) 327-4253

UTAH
Utah Alliance for the Mentally Ill
156 Westminster Avenue
Salt Lake City, UT 84115
(801) 484-3314

VERMONT
Alliance for the Mentally Ill,
   Vermont
9 Andrews Avenue
So. Burlington, VT 05401
(802) 655-2525

VIRGINIA
Virginia Alliance for the Mentally
   Ill
4010 W. Franklin Street
Richmond, VA 23221
(804) 358-6980

WASHINGTON
Alliance for the Mentally Ill of
   Washington State
12920 N.E. 14th Street
Vancouver, WA 98684
(206) 892-6323

WEST VIRGINIA
South Branch Valley Alliance for
   the Mentally Ill
Rt. 2, Box 24
Moorefield, WV 26836
(304) 434-2443

WISCONSIN
Alliance for the Mentally Ill of
   Wisconsin, Inc.
1245 E. Washington Avenue
Suite 212
Madison, WI 53703
(608) 257-5888

WYOMING
Wyoming Alliance for the Mentally
   Ill
1123 Beaumont Dr.
Casper, WY 82601
(307) 234-4775

•   •   •   •

PUERTO RICO
Puerto Rico Psychiatric Society
MEPSI Center
Call Box 6089
Bayamon, Puerto Rico 00621
(809) 793-3030

Asociacion Familiares y Voluntarios
   Pro-Participantes Centro
   Psicosacirol de Baya mon
Antiguo Hosp. Ruis Soler
Carr. #2
Bayamon, Puerto Rico 00619

VIRGIN ISLANDS
St. Croix Concerned Citizens for
   Mental Health, Inc.
P.O. Box 937 Kings Hill
St. Croix, VI 00850

CANADA

Ontario District Branch of the
  American Psychiatric Association
600 University Avenue, #918
Toronto, Ontario, Canada M5G 1X5
(416) 586-4545

Quebec & Eastern Canada District
  Branch of the American
  Psychiatric Association
Gilles C. Plante, M.D.
111 Brittany Avenue, Mont-Royal
Montreal, PQ Canada H3P 1A7
(514) 525-8576

Western Canada District Branch of
  the American Psychiatric
  Association
Nady El-Guebaly, M.D.
Dept. of Psych.,
St. Boniface Hospital
409 Tache Avenue
Winnipeg, MB Canada R2H 2A6
(204) 233-8563

Association of Relatives & Friends
  of the Mentally and Emotionally
  Ill
P.O. Box 322, Snowdon Branch
Montreal, Quebec, Canada H3X3T6
(514) 937-5351

FURTHER READING

Atkinson, Jacqueline M. *Schizophrenia: A Guide for Sufferers and Their Families*. Wellingborough, England: Turnstone Press, 1985.

Barnes, Deborah M. "Biological Issues in Schizophrenia." *Science*, January 23, 1987.

Bernheim, Kayla F., and Richard R. Lewine, *Schizophrenia: Symptoms, Causes, Treatments*. New York: Norton, 1979.

Dearth, Nona, Barbara J. Labenski, M. Elizabeth Mott, and Lillian M. Pellegrini. *Families Helping Families: Living with Schizophrenia*. New York: Norton, 1986.

Goleman, Daniel. "Aid in Day-to-Day Life Seen as Hope for Schizophrenics." *New York Times*, March 19, 1986.

Goodwin, Donald W., M.D., and Samuel B. Guze, M.D. *Psychiatric Diagnosis*. 3d ed. New York: Oxford University Press, 1984.

Green, Hannah. *I Never Promised You a Rose Garden*. New York: Holt, Rinehart & Winston, 1964.

Harding, Courtenay M., Joseph Zubin, and John S. Strauss. "Chronicity in Schizophrenia: Fact, Partial Fact, or Artifact?" *Hospital and Community Psychiatry* 38 (May 1987): 477–486.

Kaplan, Bert, ed. *The Inner World of Mental Illness*. New York: Harper & Row, 1964.

Schmeck, Harold M., Jr. "Schizophrenia Focus Shifts to Dramatic Changes in Brain." *New York Times*, March 18, 1986.

Sheehan, Susan. *Is There No Place on Earth for Me?* New York: Random House, 1983.

Snyder, Solomon H., M.D. *Biological Aspects of Mental Disorder*. New York: Oxford University Press, 1980.

Torrey, E. Fuller, M.D. *Surviving Schizophrenia: A Family Manual.* New York: Harper & Row, 1983.

Tsuang, Ming T., M.D. *Schizophrenia: The Facts.* New York: Oxford University Press, 1982.

Walsh, Maryellen. *Schizophrenia: Straight Talk for Family and Friends.* New York: Morrow, 1985.

Wilson, Louise. *This Stranger, My Son.* New York: Putnam, 1968.

Young, Patrick. *Mental Disturbances.* New York: Chelsea House, 1987.

PICTURE CREDITS

GLOSSARY

affective illness any of the mental disorders involving mood distortions, such as depression and manic-depression

antipsychotics drugs used to treat serious psychological disorders such as schizophrenia; also called neuroleptics or major tranquilizers

brief reactive psychosis mental disorder characterized by schizophrenialike symptoms that occur suddenly, last only a few days, and disappear; not considered a true schizophrenia

catatonic schizophrenia category of the disorder characterized by abnormal body behaviors that range from almost complete immobility to excited motion

chlorpromazine first of the antipsychotic medications used to treat schizophrenia; sold as Thorazine

chromosomes the rodlike structures in the nucleus of mammalian cells that contain the genes; each human cell contains 46 chromosomes

clinical psychologist a person trained to test and counsel people with mental and emotional disorders; psychologists are not physicians

concordance the existence of a disease in both members of a set of twins

delusions false beliefs; often the result of a psychological disorder

dementia praecox name given by Emil Kraepelin to what is now called schizophrenia

depression most common of the serious mental illnesses; characterized by a low mood extending over months, often with a sense of worthlessness and hopelessness

dopamine a neurotransmitter chemical in the brain suspected to play an important role in schizophrenia

electroconvulsive therapy treatment for depression in which brief pulses of electricity are passed through the brain; formerly used unsuccessfully to treat schizophrenics

frontal lobotomy surgical removal of parts of the front of the brain; formerly used unsuccessfully to treat schizophrenics

genes bits of material—contained on the chromosomes in cells—that are responsible for inherited traits; there are an estimated 50,000 to 100,000 genes in each human body

hallucinations hearing, seeing, smelling, tasting, or feeling things that are not there

hebephrenic (disorganized) schizophrenia category of the disorder characterized by silly behavior, gradual onset, and little hope of significant remission

hippocampus a part of the brain involved in governing the emotions

insulin coma a coma resulting from excessive insulin; formerly used unsuccessfully to treat schizophrenics

major tranquilizer antipsychotic drug

mania mental disorder characterized by euphoria, hyperactivity, a gushing flight of ideas, and poor judgment

manic depression mental disorder in which a person's mood alternates between very high (mania) and very low (depression)

neuroleptic antipsychotic drug

neurotransmitter a chemical that helps pass messsages from one nerve cell to another

paranoid schizophrenia a kind of schizophrenia characterized by anxiety, anger, violent behavior, and delusions of persecution or grandeur

psychiatrist a physician especially trained to treat mental and emotional illnesses

psychoanalysis a method of treating mental illnesses developed by Sigmund Freud; its basic theory is that the key to mental disorders lies in the unconscious mind

psychosomatic illness a physical disorder that is caused or significantly influenced by a person's emotional state

psychotherapy treatment that uses psychological techniques and interpersonal communications to treat mental and emotional disorders

receptors molecules on the surface of cells that a chemical—such as a neurotransmitter—must attach to before it can have any effect on the cell

schizo-affective psychosis mental illness with features of schizophrenia and affective illness; regarded as more akin to manic depression than schizophrenia

schizophrenia mental disorder in which a person loses touch with reality; characterized by profound emotional withdrawal and bizarre behavior; often includes delusions and hallucinations

schizophreniform mental disorder with schizophrenialike symptoms that last longer than a week, but less than six months; not considered true schizophrenia

schizophrenigenic schizophrenia-causing

tardive dyskinesia condition that occurs in 10 to 15% of those taking antipsychotics for long periods; common symptoms are repetitive, involuntary movements of the tongue, mouth, and face

Thorazine chlorpromazine

undifferentiated schizophrenia mixture of symptoms of catatonic, hebephrenic, and/or paranoid schizophrenias

INDEX

Patrick Young, science and medical correspondent for the Newhouse News Service in Washington, D. C., has explored the world and work of scientists and physicians for nearly two decades. In 1979, he served on the senior staff of the presidential commission that investigated the nuclear power plant accident at Three Mile Island. He is the author of *Drugs & Pregnancy* and *Mental Disturbances* in Series 2 of the ENCYCLOPEDIA OF PSYCHOACTIVE DRUGS, published by Chelsea House. He has won more than a dozen national awards for his articles on medicine, the physical sciences, and space.

Solomon H. Snyder, M.D., is Distinguished Service Professor of Neuroscience, Pharmacology, and Psychiatry and director of the Department of Neuroscience at the Johns Hopkins University School of Medicine. He has served as president of the Society for Neuroscience and in 1978 received the Albert Lasker Award in Medical Research for his discovery of opiate receptors in the brain. Dr. Snyder is a member of the National Academy of Sciences and a Fellow of the American Academy of Arts and Sciences. He is the author of *Drugs and the Brain, Uses of Marijuana, Madness and the Brain, The Troubled Mind,* and *Biological Aspects of Mental Disorder.* He is also the general editor of Chelsea House's ENCYCLOPEDIA OF PSYCHOACTIVE DRUGS.

C. Everett Koop, M.D., Sc.D., is Surgeon General, Deputy Assistant Secretary for Health, and Director of the Office of International Health of the U.S. Public Health Service. A pediatric surgeon with an international reputation, he was previously surgeon-in-chief of Children's Hospital of Philadelphia and professor of pediatric surgery and pediatrics at the University of Pennsylvania. Dr. Koop is the author of more than 175 articles and books on the practice of medicine. He has served as surgery editor of the *Journal of Clinical Pediatrics* and editor-in-chief of the *Journal of Pediatric Surgery.* Dr. Koop has received nine honorary degrees and numerous other awards, including the Denis Brown Gold Medal of the British Association of Paediatric Surgeons, the William E. Ladd Gold Medal of the American Academy of Pediatrics, and the Copernicus Medal of the Surgical Society of Poland. He is a Chevalier of the French Legion of Honor and a member of the Royal College of Surgeons, London.